ALEX G. SMITH

Department of Physics and Astronomy
University of Florida

RADIO EXPLORATION OF THE SUN

Published for
The Commission on College Physics

D. VAN NOSTRAND COMPANY, INC.

Princeton, New Jersey

Toronto   *London*

Van Nostrand Regional Offices: *New York, Chicago, San Francisco*

D. Van Nostrand Company, Ltd., *London*

D. Van Nostrand Company (Canada), Ltd., *Toronto*

PRINTED IN THE UNITED STATES OF AMERICA

To My Mother

Preface

This book is about the sun. It is also about physics, for in the sun we find atomic, nuclear, and electromagnetic phenomena taking place on a scale we can never hope to duplicate in the laboratory. Indeed, solar physics is a remarkable vehicle for bringing together most of the important ideas of modern physics. Before we are through we shall have had to think carefully about atomic spectra and nuclear fusion. We shall have dealt with plasmas and with the concepts of magnetohydrodynamics, the intriguing new science that describes the behavior of ionized gases in magnetic fields. We shall discover exotic ways to generate radio waves—cyclotron emission, the synchrotron process, Cerenkov radiation, bremsstrahlung. Hopefully, we shall gain some insight into the way scientists put such ideas together as they attempt to explain complex natural phenomena.

Like its companion volume, *Radio Exploration of the Planetary System,* this book assumes that the reader has some familiarity with physics at the level of the usual beginning course. Other than that, there are no prerequisites. Especially in discussing instrumentation, I have emphasized analogies with optics, since most people are more familiar with light and with optical instruments than they are with radio devices. I make no claim of completeness, for this small volume is not intended to be encyclopedic. In a field where there are almost as many theories as there are theorists, it would be easy to point to important omissions. For these I apologize. It is also true that radio astronomy is advancing with such breath-taking rapidity that to-day's "fact" may well become tomorrow's fallacy. If this were not so I should long ago have left the field for more exciting horizons.

Many dedicated people contributed to the making of this book. Mrs. Lee Potzner and Mrs. Betty Keyser reproduced the several versions of the manuscript with the editorial advice of Helen S.

Haines. The numerous line drawings reflect the skill and patience of Mr. W. W. Richardson, while Mr. Hans Schrader helped to prepare the photographs. My assistant, Mr. Robert Leacock, busied himself with every phase of the project. I am especially grateful to the many colleagues from whose work I have so freely drawn—although not, I fervently hope, without giving due credit. Because the facilities of the University of Florida Radio Observatory contributed a great deal to the production of the manuscript, I should be remiss if I failed to thank our sponsors, the National Science Foundation, the National Aeronautics and Space Administration, the Office of Naval Research, and the Army Research Office (Durham).

ALEX G. SMITH

Table of Contents

1   *How It Began*

"What is history but a fable agreed upon?"
NAPOLEON

Perhaps the most surprising thing about the discovery of radio waves from the sun is that it took so long. For nearly half a century scientists, engineers, and even amateur tinkerers performed experiments that, at least in principle, were capable of detecting the more spectacular outbursts of solar radio energy. Yet the final discovery somehow eluded them all. In this chapter we shall review the early history of solar radio astronomy and find that it is a narrative of near misses and inspiration gone astray, of overlooked opportunities and failure to recognize the goal even when it had been achieved. But before we become too smug, let us ask ourselves what wonders are lying unnoticed before our own eyes!

THE DISCOVERY OF RADIO WAVES

Near the middle of the last century the British theoretician J. Clerk Maxwell began a study of electromagnetic phenomena that was to become a milestone of classical physics. To a large extent Maxwell's work had its roots in the brilliant experiments and clever intuition of his fellow countryman, Michael Faraday, who clearly ranks among the great experimentalists of all time. Faraday, however, was not mathematically inclined and he had never expressed his ideas in the precise language of the mathematician.

In the process of giving mathematical form to Faraday's highly useful concepts of electric and magnetic fields, Maxwell came to the surprising conclusion that a change in an electric field must give rise to a magnetic field, while, conversely, a change in a magnetic field should create an electric field. Still more startling was the realization that such changing fields would, in effect, feed upon one another and propagate themselves through space in the form of a *wave,* with the electric and magnetic forces oscillating at right angles to each other and to the direction of travel. Maxwell's equations even predicted the speed of such a disturbance, which, curiously enough, turned out to be equal to the number of electrostatic units of charge contained in an electromagnetic unit of charge. Now, the ratio of these units had been measured in the laboratory a few years earlier, and Maxwell was thus able to predict that his waves should propagate themselves through empty space with a velocity of about 3.1×10^{10} cm/sec, which was, within experimental error, just the speed of light as it was then known. To Maxwell it seemed obvious that the long-debated question, "What is light?" had finally been resolved; light must be an electromagnetic wave. Nevertheless, many other scientists remained completely unconvinced, and even at the time of Maxwell's untimely death in 1879 his electromagnetic theory was at best making slow progress toward general acceptance.

Fortunately the theory received new and powerful support from the experiments of a young German physicist, Heinrich Hertz, who in 1888 succeeded in producing electromagnetic waves in the laboratory by purely electrical means. Hertz's apparatus, which is shown in Fig. 1-1, was based on the discovery of the American Joseph Henry that a spark discharge produces an oscillating current. In Hertz's transmitter a resonant circuit was formed by the capacitance of the plates PP and the inductance of the straight rods RR. Each time the high voltage from the induction coil caused a spark to jump the gap G, the circuit oscillated at a frequency of many millions of cycles per second (Mc/sec) until all of the energy had been radiated away in electromagnetic waves or consumed in the electrical resistance of the circuit. To detect the emitted waves, Hertz merely formed a metal rod into a ring about a foot in diameter. The ends of the rod were not quite in contact, leaving a narrow gap that displayed a stream of tiny sparks when the circuit was set into sufficiently strong oscillation by exposure to electromagnetic radiation.

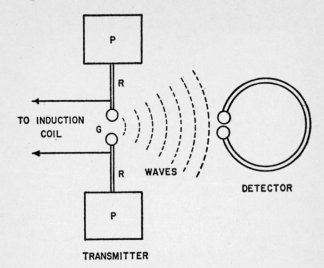

FIG. 1-1 A diagram of the apparatus with which Hertz demonstrated the existence of electromagnetic waves.

With this simple detector Hertz was able to show that his transmitter was radiating energy into the surrounding space. He further demonstrated that the radiation had unmistakable wave-like properties. When a large sheet of metal was set up as a reflector some distance in front of the transmitter, the radiated and reflected waves interfered with each other to produce a pattern of "standing waves" or alternating regions of maximum and minimum electric intensity, and by measuring the distance between these regions Hertz found that the wavelength of his radiation was about 5 m. The waves also proved to be *polarized* —that is, the electric field was vibrating in a single, well-defined plane—for the detector showed a maximum response when the plane of its loop was parallel to the rods of the transmitter, as we see it in Fig. 1-1, and no response at all when this plane was perpendicular to the rods. Here again was an obvious analogy with light waves, for which polarization effects had long been recognized and studied.* Hertz's research provided a firm experimental basis for Maxwell's theory of electromagnetism;

* See, for example, Momentum No. 7, *Polarized Light,* by W. A. Shurcliff and S. S. Ballard.

even more important, it laid the foundations of a vast new area of science and technology, for his waves lay in that part of the electromagnetic spectrum that we now associate with radio and television.

THE EARLIEST EFFORTS TO DETECT SOLAR RADIO SIGNALS

The impetus that Hertz's experiments gave to basic research is strikingly illustrated by the fact that within a dozen years of his discovery at least three groups of scientists had attempted to detect "Hertzian waves" from the sun, which seems to have had immediate appeal as a likely source of naturally occurring radio signals. It is possible that the first search for these signals was proposed in a letter written in 1890 by Professor A. E. Kennelly, an associate of the famous American inventor Thomas Edison:

I may mention that Mr. Edison, who does not confine himself to any single line of thought or action, has lately decided on turning a mass of iron ore in New Jersey, that is mined commercially, to account in the direction of research in Solar physics. . . . Along with the electromagnetic disturbances we receive from the sun which, of course, you know we recognize as light and heat . . . it is not unreasonable to suppose that there will be disturbances of much longer wavelength. If so, we might translate them into sound. Mr. Edison's plan is to erect on poles round the bulk of the ore, a cable of seven carefully insulated wires, whose final terminals will be brought to a telephone or other apparatus. It is then possible that violent disturbances in the sun's atmosphere might so disturb either the normal electromagnetic flow of energy we receive, or the normal distribution of magnetic forces on this planet, as to bring about an appreciably great change in the flow of magnetic induction embraced by the cable loop. . . .[1]

There is no record of any result from this experiment, and it is not entirely clear from Kennelly's letter that Edison was actually thinking of radio waves.

In England, meanwhile, Sir Oliver Lodge was duplicating and extending Hertz's observations. For the relatively insensitive spark-gap detector, Lodge substituted a much more effective coherer that he had developed. This device was based on the curious discovery that the high electrical resistance resulting from poor contact between metallic conductors could suddenly be reduced by exposure to electromagnetic waves. A common form of the coherer was nothing more than a glass tube a few inches long, loosely filled with metal chips or filings, and capped at the ends with metal contacts. The resistance of such a tube might decrease from many thousands of ohms to only a few ohms when a nearby spark transmitter was activated, with the change being detected by means of a sensitive galvanometer connected in series with the coherer and a battery. One problem was that the device could be restored to its original state and made ready for detection again only through the rather clumsy process of mechanically tapping the tube.

By 1894 Lodge's coherers were capable of detecting spark discharges half a mile away, and he was encouraged to remark in a public lecture on radio waves, "I hope to try for long-wave radiation from the sun, filtering out the ordinary well-known waves by a blackboard or other sufficiently opaque substance." In a later note he reported the results of this experiment:

I did not succeed in this, for a sensitive coherer in an outside shed unprotected by the thick walls of a substantial building cannot be kept quiet for long. I found its spot of light liable to frequent weak and occasionally violent excursions, and I could not trace any of these to the influence of the sun. There were evidently too many terrestrial sources of disturbance in a city like Liverpool to make the experiment feasible. . . . Clearly the arrangement must be highly sensitive in order to succeed.[2]

Although Lodge did not say, it is likely that his coherer was most sensitive to radiation of 10 or 20 cm wavelength, since he mentioned wavelengths in this range in connection with a number of other experiments.

A similar but more highly refined experiment was carried out at Potsdam by the Germans J. Wilsing and J. Scheiner. As their coherer, Wilsing and Scheiner used a piece of steel wire a few centimeters long, laid loosely on top of two similar wires that were connected to a galvanometer and a battery. To exclude interference the entire apparatus was enclosed in a metal box, and the radiation that was to be measured was introduced through an aperture. After a series of laboratory tests had indicated that their detector was highly sensitive to artificially generated electric waves, the two scientists turned their attention to the sun. On eight days in June and July of 1896 they exposed their coherer to solar radiation reflected into the box by a mirror covered with black paper to eliminate optical radiation. In the end, Wilsing and Scheiner were forced to report that, "These experiments gave no positive results." However, they remained convinced of the probable "presence of electric radiation in the ray complex sent to us by the sun," and they were inclined to blame the failure of their experiment on the earth's atmosphere, which, they felt, might have served as a screen to prevent the solar signals from reaching the ground.[3]

This warning was not lost on Charles Nordmann, a graduate student at the University of Paris who set out to improve on the work of the two Germans. In order to get above as much of the troublesome atmosphere as possible, Nordmann set up his equipment on a glacier at an altitude of 3100 m, remarking with a certain show of bravado that only bad weather had prevented him from working at the summit of Mount Blanc itself. His rather conventional detector consisted of the familiar battery, galvanometer, and coherer. Nordmann, however, made one important addition that might have led to success where others had failed; to the coherer he attached a long antenna wire, which ran horizontally across the glacier for 175 m. As Fig. 1-2 indicates, the circuit was partially immersed in mercury during adjustment to shield the coherer and short-circuit the antenna. When a measurement was to be made the mercury level was lowered, thus exposing the sensitive coherer and activating the antenna.

Surprisingly, Nordmann made observations on only a single day, September 19, 1901, and the results of the experiment were entirely negative.[4] Nordmann's apparent impatience is especially hard to understand since it is evident from his later discussion that he was not expecting a steady radio emission from the sun but, rather, violent outbursts associated with solar storms. With truly remarkable foresight he predicted that such storms must be related to the presence of sunspots, and he lamented the fact

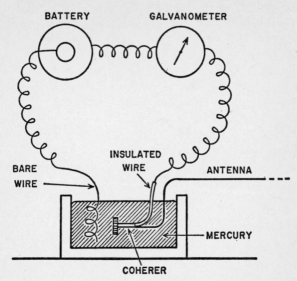

FIG. 1-2 Nordmann's apparatus for detecting solar radio waves. Two coherers were tried; one was a simple tube of nickel filings, the other a tube holding 30 steel balls with a screw at one end for adjustment of the pressure between the balls. (After C. Nordmann.[4])

that the year 1901 fell at a minimum in the well-known 11-year cycle of sunspot activity. In retrospect, it seems possible that Nordmann might have detected a few of the strongest solar radio outbursts, and thus have gained fame as the world's first successful radio astronomer, had he employed his equipment with patience during a period near sunspot maximum.

THE EFFECT OF A THEORY

The year after Nordmann's experiment, the German physicist Max Planck announced a radical new theory which, for the first time, correctly described the way the energy radiated by a hot body varies with wavelength. The new theory was the quantum theory, and, as we all know, it proved to be of enormous importance in dealing with phenomena on the atomic scale. It also enabled scientists to compute the amount of "thermal" radio energy that might be expected from the sun, and the result was completely discouraging. As the pioneer radio engineer G. C. Southworth later wrote, "The outlook for many years was not, however, promising. Calculations based on Planck's theory indicated that even at the highest radio frequencies, and with antennas of the highest directivity then available, the intensity would probably be far below the noise level prevailing in the local radio receiver." [5]

The history of science provides numerous examples of the stifling effect that the improper use of theory can have on experimentation. It may be that Planck's theory discouraged further serious attempts to observe the sun during four decades in which equipment that was quite capable of detecting solar radio outbursts was being perfected. The difficulty was not with the theory itself, but with the erroneous assumption that the sun emits only thermal radiation. As we shall see, Charles Nordmann was entirely correct in predicting powerful *nonthermal* radio emission arising from transient solar storms, and we now know that such outbursts can be millions of times more intense than the simple heat radiation of the Planck theory.

Throughout the early days of commercial radio, countless operators, amateur as well as professional, must have listened to the crescendo of a solar noise burst without suspecting its origin. During the 1930s alert experimenters discovered that a complete blackout of short-wave reception often followed visible disturbances on the face of the sun, and they guessed correctly that this must be due to the bombardment of the earth's ionosphere by some form of enhanced solar radiation. In a number of instances observers reported that such fadeouts had been preceded by an interval of increased radio noise, indicating that they had unwittingly listened to the solar radio outburst that often heralds a severe ionospheric disturbance. For example, in 1937 J. H. Dellinger wrote, "The suddenness of the radio fadeouts has astonished many radio observers, operators, and amateurs. Radio signals being received suddenly begin to diminish and the intensity falls to zero, usually within a minute. The effect is on some occasions preceded by a short period of unusually violent fading, echoes, and noise (of a type different from atmospherics). . . ." [6]

The following year D. W. Heightman commented, "During abnormal activity there is an emission of particles from the sun. . . . At such times the writer has often observed the reception of a peculiar radiation, mostly on frequencies over 20 Mc/sec, which in a receiver takes the form of a smooth though loud 'hissing' sound. This is presumably caused by the arrival of charged particles on the aerial." [7] Like his contemporaries, Heightman seemed to go out of his way to avoid the simple conclusion that the radio noise might have come directly from the sun, and he preferred instead to invent a rain of charged particles that could not in any event have penetrated the atmosphere to reach his antenna! Curiously enough, these observations followed by some years Jansky's accidental discovery that short-wave radio signals from the Milky Way do reach the earth. It is perhaps indicative of the general indifference to Jansky's pioneering work that the radio experimenters of the 1930s were unable to make what seems to us an obvious connection.

SUCCESS AT LAST

On the afternoon of February 26, 1942, a number of British radar sets began to experience strong interference of an unfamiliar nature. Throughout the next two days the trouble persisted at widely separated sites over the entire radar band from 55 to 80 Mc/sec. Because the German fleet had been active in the Channel just a few days earlier, there was considerable apprehension among the British that the Germans might be "jamming" the radars as a prelude to a major offensive. An operational research team under the direction of the young scientist Stanley Hey was hurriedly called in to investigate the problem.

Hey immediately set about determining the compass direction —or, in radar parlance, the "bearing"—from which the interference was coming. Some time later he described in his own words the totally unexpected result:

The operators determined the bearing according to the normal practice for finding the direction of a source of interference. It was found that the bearings moved throughout the day, and were always within a few degrees of that of the sun. The most striking results came from

two sites about 150 miles apart, where the elevation was also measured. Observers on these sites were able to follow the noise source con-
tinually in bearing and elevation, and observations through the
equipment telescope confirmed that their equipment was directed at the
sun. . . . The noise was not observed at night at any station. These
results show that the noise must have been caused by the direct propagation of electromagnetic noise radiations from the sun.[8]

Hey's words, written in the calm, precise language of the scientist, signaled the end of a search that had begun half a century
earlier. He was quick to note that the observed disturbance
could not have been the feeble thermal signal predicted by
Planck's theory, since it was "of the order of 10^5 times that corresponding to the calculated black-body radiation." Hey even
surmised—correctly, as we now know—that "This unusual intensity . . . appears to have been associated with the occurrence
of a big solar flare reported to be in a central position on February 28, 1942." After a lapse of 41 years, Charles Nordmann's
inspired guess attributing the emission of strong radio noise to
solar disturbances had been confirmed.

Just four months later G. C. Southworth and A. P. King of
the Bell Telephone Laboratories, independently detected solar
radio waves. As one facet of the huge wartime radar effort, the
two scientists were engaged in developing sensitive receivers for
the microwave region. Calculations based on the Planck theory
suggested to Southworth that such receivers *might* be capable of
detecting thermal radiation from the sun, and as he later wrote,
"After we had groomed a double-detection receiver to give a
relatively low first-detector noise, it was almost natural that we
should point the antenna at the sun. . . . We found, as expected, that the solar noise represented a small increase in the
total noise output." [5] This initial experiment was performed at
a frequency of 9400 Mc/sec, with the comparatively small 5-ft
parabolic "dish" antenna shown in Plate I.

At first Southworth believed that his measurements had confirmed the temperature of 6000° K that optical astronomers had
long quoted for the surface of the sun. However, a mistake was
found in his calculations and the corrected radio temperature
turned out to be nearer 20,000° K. Nevertheless, as we shall see

in Chapter 4, the microwave energy that he had recorded was almost entirely thermal in origin. Thus, within a period of only four months, Hey had identified the powerful but intermittent outbursts of radio energy that are associated with the "disturbed" sun, while Southworth had found the long-sought thermal radio waves from the "quiet" sun. The groundwork had been laid for the science of solar radio astronomy.

Through an ironic quirk of fate neither Hey nor Southworth was the first to announce to the world the detection of solar radio waves. Because of wartime restrictions Southworth's work was kept secret until April of 1945, only a month before the final German surrender, and it was even later when Hey's observations were revealed to the public. In the meantime a dedicated amateur had "scooped" both of them. Inspired by Karl Jansky's discovery of radio signals from the Milky Way, Grote Reber had constructed an antenna in the form of a parabolic reflector 31 ft in diameter in his back yard at Wheaton, Illinois. In 1943, after years of patient experimentation, he finally perfected a receiver that was sensitive enough in combination with his antenna to make an effective radio map of the Milky Way at a frequency of 160 Mc/sec, and in September of that year he easily detected the sun, although he complained that, "During these years, the sun was at low activity and the solar traces were all very much alike and uninteresting." [9] Reber's results were published in an astronomical journal in 1944.

Thus, by the end of the War the stage had been set for a radio assault on the many outstanding problems of solar physics. This time astronomers did not repeat the mistake that had been made 15 years earlier in ignoring Jansky's observations of the Milky Way. The British and the Australians were especially quick to exploit the new technique, and scientists in other nations were not far behind. It has been estimated that as much as one-third of the total effort in the rapidly expanding science of radio astronomy has been devoted to studies of the sun. In the chapters that follow we shall look at some of the more exciting results of this work. And since it is impossible to discuss solar radio emission in a meaningful way without relating it to the structure of the sun itself, we shall begin with a brief review of solar physics. Perhaps the reader should remind himself from time to time that our sun is merely an ordinary, John Doe sort of star, typical of some 10^{20} stars that populate the visible universe. Thus, as a bonus, whatever we learn about the sun is immediately applicable to an inconceivably vast horde of similar objects!

REFERENCES

1. Kennelly, A. E., quoted in J. Astron. Soc. Pacific **70**, 303-304 (1958).
2. Lodge, O. J., *Signalling Across Space Without Wires* ("The Electrician" Printing and Publishing Company, Ltd., London, 1906), 4th ed., p. 33.
3. Wilsing, J. and Scheiner, J., "On an Experiment to Prove the Existence of an Electrodynamic Radiation from the Sun," Ann. Phys. Chem. **59**, 782-792 (1896).
4. Nordmann, C., *Essai Sur le Role des Ondes Hertziennes en Astronomie Physique* (Gauthier-Villars, Paris, 1903), pp. 6-11.
5. Southworth, G. C., *Forty Years of Radio Research* (Gordon and Breach, New York, 1962), pp. 249-250.
6. Dellinger, J. H., "Sudden Disturbances of the Ionosphere," J. Res. Natl. Bur. Std. **19**, 111-141 (1937).
7. Heightman, D. W., "The Ultra High Frequencies," Wireless World **24**, 356-357 (1938).
8. Appleton, Sir E. and Hey, J. S., "Solar Radio Noise," Phil. Mag. **37**, 73-84 (1946).
9. Reber, G., "Early Radio Astronomy at Wheaton, Illinois," Proc. Inst. Radio Engrs. **46**, 15-23 (1958).

2 *Physics of the Sun*

"His rash fierce blaze of riot cannot last,
For violent fires soon burn out themselves."
SHAKESPEARE, *Richard* II

EARLY CONCEPTS OF THE SUN

Even those who have forgotten that Helios was the sun god of ancient Greece may recall the legend of his half-mortal son, Phaedron. Jealous of his father's exalted role in driving the sun-chariot across the sky each day, Phaedron tricked Helios into surrendering the reins to him for one of these dangerous journeys. The inexperienced youth was unable to control his fiery steeds and the chariot plunged wildly to earth, setting great fires as it careened across the landscape. In order to halt the catastrophe, the gods were obliged to annihilate Phaedron and his chariot with a mighty thunderbolt hurled down from the heights of Mount Olympus.

While we know that many Greek scientists took a less romantic view of the sun, this legend is typical of the concepts prevalent among early peoples, most of whom worshipped the sun as a god or as a sacred object guided by a very special deity. The Sumerians also believed that their sun god Shamash was driven across the sky in a chariot, one wheel of which represented the disc of the sun, and a similar solar chariot was supposed to convey the Hindu god Indra from east to west. Predictably, perhaps, since he was the creature of a river people, the powerful Egyptian sun god Ra made his daily journeys in a boat!

That primitive man should have deified the sun is easily understood, for it was his only source of light and heat. We can readily sympathize with his desire to propitiate and to influence such a potent force. When he turned to systematic agriculture some 5000 years ago, early Neolithic man became still more dependent upon the sun, and he was even obliged to invent the rudiments of astronomy in order to predict the seasons. Many of the earliest temples, pyramids, and monuments had astronomical significance, their remains often showing that they were carefully oriented for making astronomical observations.

Evidently an aura of mysticism surrounded the sun as late as the seventeenth century, for in 1612 Galileo's announcement of the existence of sunspots drew down upon him the criticism of scholars and clergy alike. In the popular view of the day, the sun was "immaculate" and had, therefore, to be without blemish.

Somewhat later, when the existence of sunspots had been firmly established, a number of astronomers adopted the curious view that these dusky areas were merely holes in a fiery atmosphere, through which they were able to see a cool, dark surface beneath. So strongly did the great William Herschel believe in this idea that in 1795 he wrote of the supposedly cool solar sphere, "It is most probably also inhabited, like the rest of the planets, by beings whose organs are adapted to the peculiar circumstances of that vast globe." [1]

THE MYSTERY OF SOLAR ENERGY

Eventually astronomers were driven by the weight of accumulating physical evidence to adopt more realistic models of the structure of the sun. Inevitably, their thinking was strongly influenced by the necessity of somehow accounting for the sun's enormous outpouring of energy. The magnitude of the problem can easily be illustrated by a few simple calculations based on the *solar constant H*, which is the measured value of the solar power that falls on the earth when the sun is at its average distance. In the units commonly used, $H = 2.00$ calories per square centimeter per minute; this value has been carefully corrected for atmospheric absorption, so that it refers to the unattenuated radiation that strikes the top of the earth's atmosphere.*

* A number of useful constants such as this have been collected together as Appendix 1 near the end of the book. Appendix 2 is a list of symbols and abbreviations.

How much power does this represent at the sun itself? Looking at Fig. 2-1, we see that solar energy is emitted from a surface having an area $4\pi R_0^2$. By the time it reaches the earth this same

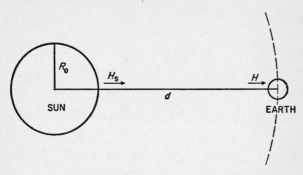

FIG. 2-1 Conversion of the solar constant H to emitted solar power H_s.

energy has spread over a much larger sphere of area $4\pi d^2$, and consequently the energy *density* has been reduced by the factor $(R_0/d)^2$. (We have, of course, derived here the well-known "inverse square law.") It follows, then, that the power per unit area at the solar surface must be

$$H_s = H(d/R_0)^2. \tag{2-1}$$

Since the distance d of the sun is 150 million kilometers (93 million miles), while its radius R_0 is 696,000 km (432,000 miles), we find that $d/R_0 = 215$ and thus

$$H_s = H(215)^2 = 9.25 \times 10^4 \text{ cal/cm}^2/\text{min} = 1541 \text{ cal/cm}^2/\text{sec}.$$

We have found that each square centimeter of the sun's surface radiates 1541 calories of energy every second. If this figure is multiplied by the total area of the sun (6.06×10^{22} cm^2), it follows that the overall solar emission is 9.34×10^{25} cal/sec or, in different units, 3.90×10^{23} kw. Little wonder that astronomers were long perplexed by the problem of accounting for such bounty!

It is perfectly natural that early scientific speculation should have regarded the sun simply as a great conflagration—that is, as a celestial bonfire sustained by the ordinary processes of combustion. Unfortunately, astronomers were long ago forced to admit that this ready explanation of solar energy is hopelessly inadequate, even though the sun is largely composed of hydrogen, a substance that releases four times the energy of the best coal when it is burned. For the sake of illustration let us make the unrealistically generous assumption that the entire mass of the sun is pure hydrogen, and that this hydrogen is somehow supplied with oxygen so that complete combustion can occur. Since the heat of combustion of hydrogen is 3.45×10^4 cal/gm, while the mass of the sun is 1.99×10^{33} gm, a total of 6.83×10^{37} cal would be produced if the sun were entirely consumed. Comparing this with the actual energy output of the sun calculated in the preceding paragraph, we see that as an extreme upper limit the combustion process could sustain the sun for only 7.32×10^{11} sec, or about 23,000 years. Needless to say, this figure is grossly inadequate in the light of fossil records which suggest that the solar constant has changed little over some *billions* of years!

When the implications of such calculations were realized, astronomers were forced to search for less obvious explanations of solar energy. For a while it was thought that sufficient energy might be generated at the sun's surface by the impact of meteorites. However, a rough upper limit on the number of such impacts can be established from the experience of the earth itself, and once again the numbers proved to be too small by many orders of magnitude.

In 1853 a more promising idea occurred to the German physicist Hermann von Helmholtz. According to Helmholtz the sun began life as a cool, diffuse ball of gas, vastly larger than its present size. The gas began to collapse inward under its own gravitational pull, and as it collapsed it grew hotter, like air that is compressed in a tire pump. Eventually a state of near-equilibrium was reached, with the pressure of the hot central gas nicely balancing the weight of the outer layers, although a continued very slow contraction of the sphere was still necessary to replace the thermal energy lost by radiation into space. Helmholtz believed that the sun is now in this phase of unobservably slow contraction. The German scientist showed that his theory could account for a solar lifetime of about 20 million years, which, in 1853, seemed entirely adequate. It was only when the weight of geological evidence showed that the age of the earth must be reckoned in *billions* of years that astronomers were once again left without an acceptable theory of solar energy. Discredited theories, however, are like bits of string—they are best saved for possible future use. It now seems likely that the contraction process does indeed play an important role in the early history of a star, and "gravitational collapse" is being widely hailed as a possible explanation of the fantastic energy of the newly discovered *quasi-stellar radio sources* or "quasars."

A final solution to the vexing problem of solar energy had to await the genius of Albert Einstein, who showed that almost limitless amounts of power could be created by the annihilation of matter itself. We shall see a little later in the present chapter how this process is believed to operate in the case of the sun.

THE STRUCTURE OF THE SUN

In order to simplify a calculation, we assumed in the preceding section that the sun is composed entirely of hydrogen. Actually, this is not a bad approximation, for spectroscopic analysis shows that about 80% of the atoms in the outer layers of the sun *are* hydrogen. Of the remaining 20%, nearly all are helium. While 64 of the familiar chemical elements have been identified in the solar spectrum, all except hydrogen and helium are present as mere traces. After helium, the most abundant elements are oxygen, nitrogen, and carbon, but each of these is present in the ratio of only one atom to about 1000 atoms of hydrogen.[2]

Since the structure of the earth itself remains moot, it may seem somewhat presumptuous to speculate about the internal details of a body 93 million miles away. Nevertheless, such speculation has proven to be scientifically fruitful, and moreover there is no doubt that we possess a great deal of accurate information about the solar *atmosphere*. Figure 2-2 represents a pie-shaped slice taken out of the sun and its atmosphere; let us begin at the center of this picture and work our way outward, pausing to inspect the various levels in some detail.

The Interior of the Sun. The central region of the sun is, in

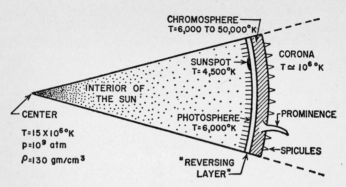

FIG. 2-2 A section of the sun and its lower atmosphere. The relative depths of the "reversing layer" and the chromosphere have been exaggerated for clarity. At the top of the photosphere the gas pressure p is about 6×10^{-3} atmosphere and the density ρ is roughly 10^{-8} gm/cm^3; for comparison the sea-level density of the earth's atmosphere is 1.3×10^{-3} gm/cm^3.

a very real sense, the "boiler room" of our solar system; here burns the celestial fire that sustains not only the sun itself, but life on the earth as well. Here at last we find the answer to the age-old question, "Where does the sun get its energy?"

Following the demise of Helmholtz's contraction theory, astronomers turned in sheer desperation to the assumption that solar power must *somehow* arise from the conversion of matter into energy. In 1905 the young Einstein placed a quantitative foundation under such speculations with his now-famous equation $E = mc^2$ (in this equation, m is of course the mass of the matter that is destroyed, c is the speed of light, and E is the energy that is released). However, the details of the process remained obscure until the 1930s, when sufficient progress had been made in nuclear physics to enable Hans Bethe and Karl von Weiszacker to spell out a plausible reaction.

It is estimated that matter near the center of the sun has a temperature of 15 million °K and a density of 130 gm/cm^3. The pressure is in the neighborhood of a billion atmospheres. Under such extreme conditions collisions between atoms are frequent and violent, and many nuclei are stripped of their protective cocoons of electrons. Circumstances are thus ripe for the production of nuclear reactions as these bare nuclei crash into each other at high speed. There is now little reason to doubt that the sun derives its energy from the conversion of hydrogen into helium, in what is called a *fusion reaction*. The basic transmutation involves the combination of four hydrogen nuclei, or protons, to form a single helium nucleus, He^4. In such a reaction it is found that the helium nucleus weighs 4.7×10^{-26} gm less than the combined weight of the original four protons, and this lost matter reappears as energy according to the relationship

$$E = mc^2 = (4.7 \times 10^{-26}\,gm)(3 \times 10^{10}\,cm/sec)^2 = 4.2 \times 10^{-5}\,erg.$$

Since it is highly improbable that four protons will collide simultaneously, it is necessary to postulate a somewhat more sophisticated chain of events for the formation of He^4. In 1938 Bethe and von Weiszacker believed that the most likely process required no less than six different reactions occurring one after the other. This sequence is known as the *carbon cycle*, because carbon enters into it as a carrier or catalyst. Nuclear astrophysicists are now convinced that while the carbon cycle may indeed dominate the energy generation of very massive stars, it plays only a secondary role in the sun, which is a star of average mass.

Under the conditions found in the central regions of the sun, the so-called *proton-proton reaction* probably generates most of the energy. The process starts with the collision of two protons (H^1) to form a nucleus of heavy hydrogen (H^2), together with a positron (e^+) and a neutrino (ν). Or, written as a nuclear equation,

$$H^1 + H^1 \rightarrow H^2 + e^+ + \nu. \tag{2-2}$$

Subsequently, the H^2 nucleus collides with another proton to form a light isotope of helium and a gamma ray:

$$H^2 + H^1 \rightarrow He^3 + \gamma. \tag{2-3}$$

The final reaction is the collision of two of the newly created He^3 nuclei to yield a nucleus of ordinary helium, plus two protons and another gamma ray:

$$He^3 + He^3 \rightarrow He^4 + H^1 + H^1 + \gamma. \tag{2-4}$$

If we look back over Eqs. (2-2), (2-3), and (2-4), we find that a total of six protons went into creating the two He^3 nuclei, but at the end we recovered two protons, so that the *net* nuclear transmutation was the desired one of $4H^1 \rightarrow He^4$.

While such a fusion reaction is self-sustaining once it gets under way, an enormously high temperature is needed to start it. This problem is, in fact, at the heart of most of the difficulties that have plagued numerous costly attempts to generate energy from fusion reactions in the laboratory. How, then, did the proton-proton process begin in the sun? It now seems likely that the initial high temperature arose through gravitational contraction of the great diffuse mass of gas that formed the primitive sun, very much as Helmholtz had predicted over a century ago!

In what form does the released nuclear energy appear? Equations (2-3) and (2-4) show that part of it appears directly as radiant energy in the guise of gamma-ray photons. The positron created in Eq. (2-2) is actually an anti-electron, which is quickly attracted to an ordinary negative electron, and the two annihilate each other in the well-known reaction

$$e^+ + e^- \rightarrow 2\gamma , \qquad\qquad (2\text{-}5)$$

releasing still more energy in the form of gamma radiation. A count shows that for each He^4 nucleus that is formed a total of seven gamma-ray photons is emitted [remember that the processes of Eqs. (2-2) and (2-3) occur *twice* during the creation of a single He^4 nucleus].

We are left, then, with a picture of the solar interior as a vast nuclear furnace in which the fuel is hydrogen at enormous temperature and pressure. As this fuel is consumed, energy streams outward in the form of gamma radiation, while helium is left behind as the "ashes" of the reaction. The gamma-ray photons are repeatedly absorbed and re-emitted as they encounter innumerable atoms on their long journey toward the surface of the sun, and in these encounters their energy is gradually degraded, first into the X-ray region of the spectrum, then into the ultraviolet, and finally into visible light and infrared radiation near the solar surface or *photosphere*. Thus it is radiation, rather than conduction or convection, that is largely responsible for carrying energy from the nuclear furnace to the surface, where it can be radiated into space; however, the violent churning that is so conspicuous in photographs of the photosphere shows that convection must become important in the outermost layers.

Strangely enough, even though they are particles the neutrinos that are produced in the proton-proton reaction [Eq. (2-2)] escape from the solar interior far more readily than do the gamma-ray photons. Because neutrinos are without charge and essentially without mass, they penetrate matter with such ghostly ease that a solid wall over 3000 light years thick would be required to stop them! As you read these words, 10^{10} solar neutrinos are passing through each square centimeter of your body every second. If we could develop a "neutrino telescope" we would at last have a means of actually peering into the interior of the sun and experimentally measuring conditions there.[3]

The Photosphere. Since the sun is a gaseous body, it is misleading to think of the photosphere as a sharp boundary like the surface of the earth. It is, rather, a shallow transition layer in which the gas pressure and density fall very rapidly with increasing altitude. At the bottom of this region the gas is completely opaque to visible light, but near the top it is highly transparent. Because its total thickness is less than 400 km, or 0.06% of the solar radius, the photospheric layer *looks* like a solid surface to the naked eye, or even to the telescope (Plate II).

Even the lowest levels of the photosphere are far less dense than the sea-level atmosphere of the earth, through which we see with such ease. Why, then, are these levels so opaque? The answer apparently lies in the presence of large numbers of the negative hydrogen ion, H^-, which is a powerful absorber of light. The name photosphere or "light-sphere" is well chosen, for most of the direct light and heat that we receive from the sun comes from this brilliant surface, which has an effective temperature of about 6000° K.

That the photosphere is a fluid is emphasized by the sun's peculiar mode of rotation. A spot on the solar equator completes one rotation in 25 days, but at latitudes 30° north or south of the equator the time required is over 26 days. For the highest latitudes at which the rotation has been measured the period is no less than 34 days! Such differential rotation would of course be impossible if the sun were a solid body.

By studying Plate II the reader may discover for himself that the "limb," or edge, of the sun is darker than the center of the disc. The reason for this *limb-darkening* is shown in Fig. 2-3.

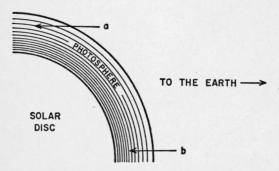

FIG. 2-3 A quadrant of the solar disc showing the relative penetration of lines-of-sight at the limb (a) and at the center of the disc (b). The thickness of the photosphere is greatly exaggerated in the diagram.

When we look obliquely into the absorbing gases of the photosphere at the edge of the sun, our line of sight does not penetrate as deeply as when we look straight down into the photosphere near the center of the disc. Now, the temperature of the photosphere falls rapidly with altitude, and at the limb we are therefore looking at a higher, cooler layer of gas—a layer which, because it *is* cooler, radiates less light and consequently seems less brilliant.

Under high magnification the photosphere takes on the mottled, "rice grain" structure seen in Plate III. A given bright granule lasts only a few minutes, and is believed to represent an upwelling of hot material that has been brought to the surface by convection. The dark lanes separating the granules are probably formed by gas that has cooled and is sinking back toward the bottom of this turbulent surface layer.

Much of our knowledge of the sun has been gained by studying its spectrum. Indeed, the great optical instruments that have been built especially for solar research are used mainly as powerful spectrographs for analyzing the sun's radiation. As we see in Plate IV, such instruments generally bear little resemblance to ordinary telescopes, for they are designed to take full advantage of the sun's unparalleled brilliance. Plate V is a photograph of the solar spectrum, which is of the type known as a "dark line absorption spectrum"; that is, it consists of a number of dark lines superimposed on a bright, continuous background. In the case of the sun the lines are referred to as "Fraunhofer lines" after the scientist who in 1814 made the first detailed map of them.

What does such a spectrum indicate about its source? Every student of physics learns a little catechism which tells him that a continuous spectrum is emitted by an incandescent solid, liquid, or gas under high pressure; he also learns that dark lines are created by interposing a relatively cool gas between such a continuous source and the spectroscope. The dark lines result because the gas absorbs from the continuous background many of the frequencies that it would emit as *bright* lines if it were excited to incandescence. It was entirely natural for solar physicists to transfer this simple concept to the sun. They pictured the photosphere as the continuous source and imagined it to be surrounded by a layer of cooler gas that produced the Fraunhofer lines. Figure 2-2 shows this region, which was known as the *reversing layer*.

Unfortunately, scientific theories have a way of growing more complex as time goes by, and in the past few years astronomers have had to retreat from the appealing simplicity of this model of the solar atmosphere. It now appears that different absorption lines are produced at different levels in the upper photosphere and lower chromosphere, so that the concept of a single well-defined reversing layer has become largely artificial. Furthermore, the lines cannot be formed merely by absorption at the resonant frequencies of the interfering atoms, for energy is not so easily disposed of. An atom that has been excited by absorbing a photon tends to reradiate its newly acquired energy within a tiny fraction of a second, and thus it is not immediately obvious that anything has really been lost from the incident radiation. How, then, are absorption lines created?

The formation of Fraunhofer lines is attributed to at least two processes, each of which results in taking energy away from the frequency of a line and spreading it over the surrounding continuum. First, an excited atom may return to its normal state in two or more steps, rather than in a single large jump; known as *fluorescence*, this mechanism results in the emission of several photons, each of which has a lower frequency than the photon that was absorbed. Second, even if the emitted photon has the same frequency as the incident photon, it will generally be radiated in a different direction, producing a powerful *scattering* effect. Many of the scattered photons will be reabsorbed by nearby H^- ions and emitted again with altered frequencies. In either case the net effect is to shift energy away from the frequency of the original absorption. The process of creating a Fraunhofer line might be likened to the home-owner who digs a hole in his yard and gets rid of the dirt he has removed by scattering it over the surrounding lawn.

The Chromosphere. For a few brief moments during a total eclipse of the sun, the overwhelming glare of the photosphere is hidden by the moon. Then the sun is seen to be rimmed by a narrow ring of reddish light arising in a layer of the solar atmosphere appropriately named the *chromosphere* or "colorsphere." This region is shown in Fig. 2-2 as a shaded band just above the reversing layer, and it can also be seen in Plate VI. In a spectroscope the chromosphere displays a bright-line *emission* spectrum, indicating that it is composed of incandescent gas at low pressure. The layer, in fact, owes its ruddy hue to the brilliance of one of these emission lines—the famous H-alpha line of hydrogen at a wavelength of 6563 Å. About 14,000 km above the photosphere the spectrum of the chromosphere fades out, and this height is consequently taken as the upper boundary of the layer.

Physically, the chromosphere is a churning sea of activity. Its gases have a fibrous structure that has been likened to the blades of grass in a dense lawn. Individual *spicules*—as the "blades" are called—constantly form and vanish; like the photospheric granules, their lives are measured in minutes. Many of the spicules first appear near the base of the chromosphere and swiftly thrust their way upward until they burst into the lower corona, giving the top of the chromosphere the jagged appearance seen in Fig. 2-2 and in Plate VI. Since there is no evidence that this upward-rushing material ever falls back into the lower atmosphere, it has been hypothesized that the spicules constantly supply the corona with new material to replace the gas that is flowing out into space as the *solar wind* (see Chapter 8).

What is the energy source that drives these violent mechanical motions in the chromosphere? Even more puzzling, what supplies the energy to raise the temperature to 50,000° K in the uppermost reaches of the layer? In thermodynamics we learn that heat always flows from a hot region to a cooler region, and yet the chromosphere is far hotter than the underlying photosphere, which is presumably its source of energy! Strangely enough, many solar physicists believe that the answer to both questions lies in *shock waves* much like the annoying and sometimes destructive "sonic booms" created by supersonic aircraft. The violent churning of the lower solar atmosphere is pictured as generating a continuous din of powerful shock waves that surge upward, driving before them the jet-like spicules and heating the thin gases of the chromosphere to temperatures far above those of the underlying photosphere.

The Corona. Plate VII shows the beautiful spectacle provided by the sun's outer atmosphere at the time of a total eclipse. Known appropriately as the *corona* (i.e., "crown"), this atmosphere stretches out into space far beyond the limits of the photograph. As we shall see in Chapter 8, it reaches even to the earth and beyond, so that in a sense we actually "live" in the solar corona!

It is evident from Plate VII that the corona is far from homogeneous. Like the lower levels of the solar atmosphere it shows evidence of a rayed or filamentary structure, with especially conspicuous "streamers" diverging from the polar regions. Even in the densest part of the corona, just above the chromosphere, there are only 10^9 particles/cm^3; we say "only" because in the sea-level atmosphere of the earth there are 3×10^{19} molecules/cm^3.

Until relatively recent times the corona could be observed only during an eclipse, for the photosphere is a million times brighter than even the innermost corona. However in 1930 the French astronomer Bernard Lyot perfected an instrument called the *coronagraph* in which an artificial eclipse is produced by covering the image of the photosphere with a metal disc.[4] Although this seems like a childishly simple idea, it requires near-perfection of both instrument and atmosphere in order to work. Since the sea-level sky in the vicinity of the sun is itself brighter than the corona, coronagraphs are found only at high-altitude mountain observatories. Even a few specks of dust on the lens of the instrument can scatter enough light to blot out the delicate corona! The ability of the coronagraph to discriminate against scattered sunlight is greatly amplified by adding a narrow-band interference filter that passes only the light of a single coronal emission line; such a filter also makes the instrument a powerful device for studying the chromosphere and the prominences.

Most of the light of the corona is simply sunlight that has been scattered by coronal electrons, but 29 emission lines have also been recorded. For decades many of these lines defied identification, and for a while some of them were even attributed to a mythical new element that was ingeniously named "coronium." In 1940 the Swedish physicist Edlén finally showed that the mysterious lines were emitted by atoms of iron, nickel, and calcium that had been stripped of as many as 13 electrons. Such a degree of ionization means that coronal temperatures must be very high indeed, and several kinds of spectroscopic evidence point to a value of about 1,000,000° K. In Chapter 4 we shall see that radio measurements provide a powerful new tool for probing the temperature of the corona at many levels.

A temperature of a million degrees makes the corona by far the hottest region of the sun within reach of our instruments. It also forces us to face again the problem that troubled us in the case of the chromosphere: Where does the energy come from to maintain such temperatures? A number of theorists have suggested that the shock waves which were invoked to heat the chromosphere might continue outward to perform a similar task in the corona.

Whatever the mechanism that heats it, the corona must approximate a pure *plasma*—that is, a gas composed entirely of positively and negatively charged ions. At a temperature of a million degrees, particles move so swiftly and collide with such violence that molecules cannot exist and individual atoms are at least partially stripped of their electrons. Since the solar atmosphere abounds in hydrogen, the coronal plasma must consist largely of protons and electrons. Like most human activities physics moves in cycles and in fashions, and in recent years the study of plasmas has surged to the fore as one of the leading branches of experimental and theoretical physics. In the sun plasma physicists have before their eyes phenomena taking place on a scale that can never be duplicated in the laboratory.

SOLAR ACTIVITY

Thus far we have treated the structure of the sun as if it were unchanging. This was merely a simplification designed to avoid confusion, for nearly everyone knows that the sun undergoes a complex 11-year cycle of activity that affects virtually all of the observable phenomena. Today scientific interest in solar activity has reached an all-time high, for it has become evident that these changes affect not only the sun itself, but the earth and other bodies in the solar system as well. Later on we shall see that the sun's performance as a radio transmitter is also intimately linked to the cycle of solar activity.

Sunspots. The great Italian physicist-astronomer Galileo is often credited with having discovered sunspots in 1610, along with the mountains of the moon, the rings of Saturn, and the moons of Jupiter. However, it is quite possible that other early users of the telescope detected sunspots some months before Galileo, and the Dutchman John Fabricius published an account of them in 1611, a year before they appeared in Galileo's writings. Since the larger sunspots are visible to the naked eye, the historical debate over which scientist first saw them in the telescope is a great deal like arguing about who "discovered" the moon! Chinese annals record naked-eye observations of sunspots going back to 28 B.C., and in a letter to a wealthy patron Galileo

himself remarked that during the reign of Charlemagne "for
eight days together the people of France saw a black spot on
the solar disc." [5]

Although the early telescopic observers noted marked fluctuations in the numbers of visible spots, the periodic nature of the
variation went unnoticed for more than two centuries. Finally,
in 1843, the German apothecary Heinrich Schwabe discovered
the *sunspot cycle*. Figure 2-4 shows the 19 cycles that have been

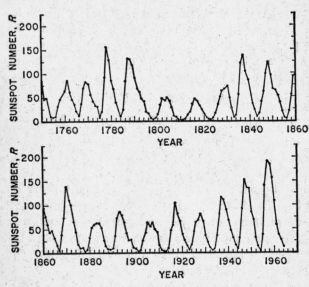

FIG. 2-4 Sunspot numbers from 1750 to 1964. The sunspot number given here and
in Eq. (2-6) is the widely used *Zurich* sunspot number.

completed since consistent telescopic records began around 1750.
The quantity plotted in the figure is the mean annual sunspot
number R. Now, contrary to what many people suppose, the
sunspot number for a given date is not simply the number of
spots that can be counted. Instead, it is given by the formula

$$R = k(f + 10g), \qquad (2-6)$$

where f is the total number of spots and g is the number of
disturbed *regions* (either single spots or groups of spots); k is a

personal factor, generally near unity, that depends upon the observer and the size of his telescope. The reader will have no trouble seeing that Eq. (2-6) gives heavy weight to the number of separate disturbed areas. If 10 spots were concentrated in a single group, R would be only 20 (assuming $k = 1$), whereas the same number of widely dispersed spots would produce a sunspot number of 110. It is evident in Fig. 2-4 that the sunspot cycle is not strictly periodic, either in time or in amplitude. The *average* interval between maxima is 11.2 years, but individual intervals have ranged from 7.3 to 17.1 years.

What can we say about the physical nature of sunspots? In size they range from tiny "pores" barely visible in a large telescope to giant disturbances 25,000 miles or more in diameter. Such variability is well illustrated in Plate II. A spot may last less than a day, or it may survive several rotations of the sun; the average lifetime is 3 or 4 days. Plate III is a photograph of a typical large sunspot, showing the dark core or *umbra* and the surrounding dusky margin or *penumbra*. Such a spot generally appears as a shallow, saucer-shaped depression in the photosphere. In a powerful spectrograph the Doppler shifts of the spectrum lines show that gases flow radially outward from the center of the saucer to its rim, and this flow, which is known as the *Evershed effect*, may reveal the secret of the spot's existence. According to a popular theory, gases rise from beneath the solar surface to the center of the spot, and from there they expand outward. As the gas molecules rise they gain potential energy at the expense of their original kinetic energy, or in other words, the gas is cooled. We might think of a sunspot as a kind of solar "refrigerator" which maintains a temperature some 1500° K below that of the surrounding photosphere. At this reduced temperature the gases of the sunspot radiate only a fraction as much light as the rest of the solar surface, and the spot consequently appears dark by comparison.

Sunspots tend to occur in belts on either side of the solar equator. During a sunspot cycle the location of these belts varies in a remarkable manner. As Fig. 2-5 shows, spots which appear early in the cycle favor regions about 30° north and south of the sun's equator. Subsequent spots tend to form at lower and lower

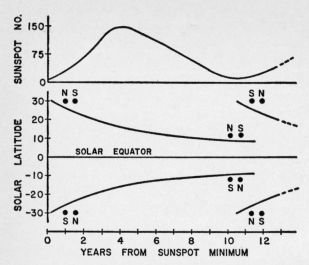

FIG. 2-5 Changes in sunspot latitude during the solar cycle. The upper curve, which is reproduced here merely for comparison, shows the familiar variation of sunspot number throughout the 11-year solar cycle. The lower curves indicate how the average latitude of sunspot formation drifts toward the sun's equator as the cycle progresses. Magnetic polarities of bipolar spots are indicated by the letters N and S, and the "leading" spot of each pair is on the left.

latitudes as the cycle progresses, until the two belts of activity are within 7° of the equator. Finally, the beginning of a new cycle is signaled by outbreaks of spots at high latitudes, perhaps even while a few spots belonging to the old cycle are still to be seen near the equator.

Faculae, Plages, and Prominences. Sunspots are merely the most conspicuous symptom of deep-rooted changes in the sun that are as yet very poorly understood. Almost invariably spots form in disturbed areas known as *active regions,* which are responsible for a great variety of other phenomena. Because many of these phenomena must be observed with highly specialized instruments, it is only recently that they have received the attention they deserve.

The birth of an active region is usually announced by the appearance of bright patches in the photosphere and chromosphere before any sunspots have become visible. As always, such brightening calls attention to the presence of a "hot spot" in the gases of the solar atmosphere. Known as *faculae,* the photospheric patches can be seen in white light with an ordinary telescope when they approach the edge of the solar disc, where the light of the surrounding photosphere has been subdued by limb darkening. A sharp-eyed reader should be able to detect a number of faculae near the limb in Plate II.

On the other hand, the overlying chromospheric brightenings, or *plages,* can be detected only in the monochromatic light of one of the stronger Fraunhofer lines. For decades it was necessary to use a complex instrument known as a *spectroheliograph* to isolate the requisite narrow band of wavelengths, but now the invention of the narrow-band interference filter has simplified the task. Several bright plage areas are shown in Plate VIII, which is a photograph of part of the solar disc made in the red light of the hydrogen-alpha line. The picture also gives a striking impression of the fibrous and turbulent structure of the sun's atmosphere. Not only do faculae and plages precede spots within a given active region—they also outlive the spots, sometimes by several months.

When a total eclipse of the sun occurs near sunspot maximum, the solar disc often appears to be ringed with giant flames leaping out into space. These are the *prominences,* and, properly viewed, they are by far the most dramatic of all solar phenomena. As Fig. 2-2 suggests, prominences extend upward from the chromosphere, typically reaching out 40,000 or 50,000 km into the corona. An occasional specimen has been observed to soar to an altitude equal to the diameter of the sun itself.

Astronomers divide prominences into two contrasting groups according to behavior. *Active prominences* lead a short but spectacular existence, developing so rapidly in the atmosphere above active regions that they often reach speeds of 500 km/sec or more. Lasting from only a few minutes to several hours, these eruptions are among the shortest-lived phenomena connected with the sunspot regions. Even a photograph as striking as Plate IX gives an inadequate impression of such a dynamic event! *Quiescent prominences,* on the other hand, typically last for many months, often appearing against the disc of the sun as dark filaments in photographs taken in monochromatic light. They change only slowly in size and shape, and show no tendency to associate with active regions.

At one time prominences, like the corona, could be seen only during the fleeting moments of a total eclipse. Under these circumstances it is perhaps understandable that as late as 1850 prominences were widely believed to belong to the moon, rather than to the sun! When the spectroscope was first applied to an eclipse in 1868 it was found that prominences emit the typical bright-line spectrum that we associate with an incandescent gas. One of the spectroscopists, P. J. C. Janssen, was so struck by the brilliance of the lines that he immediately became convinced they should be visible against the sky without benefit of an eclipse. The very next day he set the slit of his spectroscope near the sun's limb and easily observed the emission lines in full daylight. Moreover, by moving the slit he could scan across a prominence and determine its size and shape. A bit later Sir William Huggins discovered that the slit could be opened so as to take in an entire prominence, and a generation of solar spectroscopists began the laborious task of "promenading" the slits of their instruments around the solar limb in order to map the prominences. This crude technique has now been replaced by mechanically scanned slits (the spectroheliograph) and by interference filters (the coronagraph).

Because of their flame-like appearance, it is only natural to think of prominences as leaping upward from the chromosphere, and many do in fact show such motion. Others, however, mysteriously condense out of the gases of the lower corona and rain *downward* into the chromosphere. Motion-picture studies suggest that this "rain" results in a net loss of coronal material at a rate such that the entire corona must be replaced every 10 hours! Thus we arrive at a picture of the corona as a cyclic phenomenon. Material continuously streams outward in the solar wind and inward in the prominences; the loss is presumably made good by the injection of new material from the chromospheric spicules.

Flares. On September 1, 1859, two British astronomers who happened to be drawing sunspots at widely separated observatories "simultaneously saw two luminous objects, shaped something like two new moons. . . . These burst suddenly into sight at the edge of a great sunspot with a dazzling brightness at least five or six times that of the neighboring portions of the photosphere, and moved eastward over the spot in parallel lines, growing smaller and fainter, until in about five minutes they disappeared. . . ." [6] The two observers, R. C. Carrington and R. Hodgson, had witnessed the first recorded instance of a solar *flare*. This event was followed by exceptionally strong magnetic disturbances on the earth, and by brilliant displays of the aurora borealis or "northern lights." The possibility of a connection between the unusual solar phenomenon and those that followed on the earth was not overlooked by the scientists of that day. In Chapter 8 we shall see that these suspicions were well founded.

Although Carrington and Hodgson made their observations in ordinary white light, most of the light from a flare is concentrated in a few strong emission lines. It naturally follows that the disturbance is far more conspicuous in an instrument such as the coronagraph or spectroheliograph, which is capable of isolating one of these favored wavelengths. Plate X, for example, shows a flare caught near its peak in the light of the hydrogen-alpha line. Flares always occur near active regions, and they generally appear as a rapid brightening of part of an existing plage; thus they are largely creatures of the chromosphere, although it is not unusual for the disturbance to intrude into the lower corona. The most remarkable aspect of the phenomenon is the suddenness with which it occurs. In as little as one minute the flare may reach a brightness of from 4 to 15 times that of the surrounding photosphere, only to fade slowly back into obscurity during the next half hour.

We now know that large flares emit a remarkably diverse spectrum of waves and particles in addition to their outpouring of visible light. The waves run the gamut of the electromagnetic spectrum from X-rays and ultraviolet radiation to long-wavelength radio waves. The particles are largely protons and electrons, reflecting the composition of the solar atmosphere, and their kinetic energies sometimes exceed a billion electron volts. Obviously a flare can act as a giant particle accelerator, but the secret of its operation is one of the many unsolved mysteries of solar physics.

Because of the influence the flare-created waves and particles exert on the earth, and even on interplanetary space, solar flares are being studied intensively by large numbers of physicists and astronomers, and a chain of observatories maintains a world-wide "flare patrol" to detect these events. In the chapters that follow we shall repeatedly have occasion to call attention to the importance of phenomena associated with flares.

Solar Magnetic Fields. Thus far we have neglected a most important piece of evidence that may in the end prove to be the key that unlocks the secret of solar activity. The surface of the sun is permeated by a complex network of magnetic fields that seem to change in rhythm with many of the other phenomena we have been discussing. While it is still difficult to sort out cause and effect, there is now good reason to believe that the fluctuating fields are the driving force that energizes all forms of solar activity.

How does one detect a magnetic field at a distance of 150 million kilometers? The answer lies in the *Zeeman effect,* which most students of physics will remember as a splitting of spectrum lines that occurs when the source is placed in a strong magnetic field. Lines that were formerly single appear as doublets, triplets, or even more complex patterns. Since the separations of the components are proportional to the magnetic field strength, the observed Zeeman splitting can be used to determine the intensity of the field, however remote it may be. Moreover, if the spectrum is viewed through a suitable analyzer, the different components of the line show different polarizations,* and from these polarizations the *direction* of the magnetic field can be deduced.

Although broadening and even splitting of solar spectrum lines had been noticed earlier, it was not until 1908 that the noted American astrophysicist George Ellery Hale recognized

---

* Applied to electromagnetic radiation, such as light or radio waves, the term "polarization" refers to the manner in which the electric field vibrates. For a detailed discussion of polarization, the reader is referred to Momentum No. 7, *Polarized Light,* by W. A. Shurcliff and S. S. Ballard.

these effects as indicating the presence of magnetic fields on the sun. We now know that fields as strong as 4000 gauss exist in sunspots, which often occur in pairs with the two spots showing opposite magnetic polarities, like the poles of a horseshoe magnet (Fig. 2-6). Even stranger is the tendency for the "leading"

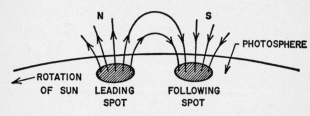

FIG. 2-6 Bipolar sunspot. In this case the leading spot displays north magnetic polarity. A number of such pairs can be seen in Plate II.

spot of each pair to show the same polarity throughout an entire hemisphere of the sun, while in the other hemisphere the polarities are reversed. This curious relationship is diagrammed in Fig. 2-5. During the complete sunspot cycle shown in the figure, leading spots in the northern hemisphere are of north polarity, while the leading spots in the southern hemisphere show south polarity. However, when spots of the *new* cycle appear at the right of the figure, these magnetic relationships are completely reversed! It is not difficult to see that the whole cycle of solar activity, including a return to the same sunspot polarity, occupies 22 years rather than 11 years.

Does the sunspot create its own magnetic field, or does the field create the spot? Which is the chicken and which the egg? Since magnetic fields usually permeate active regions *before* spots appear, it is generally assumed that the fields contribute in some way to the formation of the spots. A number of scientists now believe that the magnetic field cools the photosphere and creates a spot by inhibiting convection, thereby preventing hot material from the interior from reaching the surface. A highly conducting material, such as the solar plasma, moves with considerable difficulty across a magnetic field because of the opposing currents that are induced. Note that this theory of sunspot cooling is nearly the inverse of the earlier theory outlined in connection with the Evershed effect, which depends upon the *free* flow of gases!

Solar magnetic fields are not by any means confined to sun-spots, or even to other visible manifestations of activity. During the 1950s the father and son team of H. D. and H. W. Babcock invented a highly sensitive electronic magnetograph[7] capable of revealing very small Zeeman displacements, and this instrument showed that the whole solar surface is interlaced with a complex pattern of weak fields. Within 30° of the poles these fields seemed to display some degree of regularity, which suggested to the Babcocks that the sun has an overall dipole magnetic field similar to that of the earth. However, recent observations with improved instruments—especially those of the Soviet astronomer A. B. Severny—have shown that much of this apparent regularity resulted from inadequate resolving power in the earlier equipment, just as individual letters and words disappear and only regularly spaced lines seem to remain if you hold this page too far from your eyes. Seen under high magnetic resolution, even the polar regions of the sun become a jumble of mixed magnetic polarities.

In the magnetic fields of the sun we may behold the reservoir of energy that is unleashed when a flare occurs. A magnetic field stores energy W at the rate

$$W = \left(\frac{B^2}{8\pi}\right) \text{ergs/cm}^3, \tag{2-7}$$

where B is the field strength in gauss. Now, a large flare may release an energy of 10^{32} ergs in a volume of 10^{29} cm^3, creating a transient energy *density* of 1000 ergs/cm^3. Since this is hundreds of times greater than the thermal energy density of the corona, astronomers have been faced with a major puzzle in accounting for such a concentration of power. However, Eq. (2-7) shows that a magnetic field of only 160 gauss stores the needed energy, and such fields are common in active regions of the sun. Thus, nearly all recent theories of flares assume that they are caused by a sudden conversion of magnetic energy into heat and other forms of radiation.

Has the introduction of magnetic fields into solar physics really solved any of the mysteries of the sun, or has it merely cloaked them in a new guise? Can we hope to explain solar magnetic fields when we are still puzzled by those of our own planet? While we are still a long way from final understanding, a great deal of promise is held forth by the ideas of *magnetohydrodynamics*, a relatively new science that deals with the motions of plasmas in magnetic fields. One of the important tenets of this science is that a magnetic field tends to be "frozen into" a plasma —that is, the imbedded lines of magnetic force are dragged along with the plasma as it moves. H. W. Babcock has suggested that the faster rotation of the sun's equatorial regions may wrap lines of force around and around the sun in the lower latitudes, twisting and concentrating them into "magnetic ropes" beneath the photosphere.[8] As the continuing differential rotation stretches these ropes, they increasingly form kinks or loops which thrust up through the surface to create bipolar sunspots. Since the ropes are twisted oppositely in the two hemispheres, the reversed polarities of sunspot pairs above and below the equator are accounted for. Over an 11-year period the original lines of force slowly dissipate, but a new "unwrapped" field with reversed polarity forms from the remnants and the process begins anew. Although this picture is as yet painted with a broad brush, it is indicative of the promise that exists in some of the newer ideas of theoretical physics.

REFERENCES

1. Herschel, W., Scientific Papers I (The Royal Society and the Royal Astronomical Society, London, 1912), p. 480.
2. Menzel, D. H., *Our Sun* (Harvard University Press, Cambridge, Massachusetts, 1959), p. 95.
3. Morrison, P., "Neutrino Astronomy," Sci. Am. 207, 90-98 (August, 1962).
4. Maczaika, G. R. and Sinton, W. M., *Tools of the Astronomer* (Harvard University Press, Cambridge, Massachusetts, 1961), pp. 241-243, 248-252.
5. Galileo, G., "Letters on Sunspots," in *Discoveries and Opinions of Galileo* (Doubleday & Co., Inc., Garden City, New York, 1957), p. 117.

6. Young, C. A., *The Sun* (D. Appleton and Co., New York, 1895), pp. 120-121.
7. Babcock, H. W. and Babcock, H. D., in *The Sun,* edited by G. P. Kuiper (University of Chicago Press, Chicago, 1953), pp. 704-710.
8. Babcock, H. W., "The Topology of the Sun's Magnetic Field and the 22-Year Cycle," Astrophys. J. **133,** 572-587 (1961). See also Sky and Telescope **22,** 3 (1961).

FOR FURTHER READING

Abetti, G., *Solar Research* (Eyre and Spottiswoode, London, 1962).

Abetti, G., *The Sun* (Faber and Faber, London, 1962).

Babcock, H. W., "The Magnetism of the Sun," Sci. Am. **202,** 52-62 (February, 1960).

Ellison, M. A., *The Sun and Its Influence* (Routledge and Keegan Paul Ltd., London, 1955).

Lalou, E., *The Orion Book of the Sun* (Orion Press, New York, 1960).

Olcott, W. T., *Sun Lore of All Ages* (G. P. Putnam's Sons, Inc., New York, 1914).

Smith, H. J. and Smith, E. v. P., *Solar Flares* (The Macmillan Co., New York, 1963).

3 Instruments for Solar Radio Research

*"I grow daily to honor facts more and more,
and theory less and less."*

CARLYLE

Every workman needs proper tools. We saw in the last chapter that, even though any available telescope can be used for the purpose, optical astronomers found it profitable to develop highly specialized instruments for viewing the sun. In the same way, radio astronomers bent on studying the sun have evolved special instruments for their investigations. It is largely on these devices that we shall concentrate our attention in the present chapter, since a somewhat more generalized review of radio-astronomical instrumentation may be found in an earlier volume of this series.*

Why should the problem of observing solar radio emission differ from that of observing other objects, such as the moon, the planets, or radio galaxies? First of all, the radiation from the sun is far more powerful than that from other celestial radio sources. Thus the instrument designer can "trade off" sensitivity for other characteristics that may be more urgent. Second, the sun subtends the relatively large angle of $\frac{1}{2}°$, making it practicable to resolve the solar disc with radio telescopes of easily realizable dimensions. Finally, much of the sun's radio emission is highly sporadic, and instruments must be designed to take maximum advantage of brief periods of intense activity.

Like most celestial sources, the sun emits a radio signal of the type described as *noise*. A familiar example of such a signal

* See Momentum No. 2, *Radio Exploration of the Planetary System,* by A. G. Smith and T. D. Carr.

is the hiss that is heard in a radio or television receiver when it is tuned between stations with the volume turned up. In this case most of the noise is caused by erratic motions of electrons in the receiver circuit itself, although some of the signal may come from the Milky Way galaxy that surrounds us. Noise may be thought of as a mixture of a great number of individual frequencies, all of which are fluctuating independently and randomly in amplitude. In the case of solar radio noise we are interested in learning how it varies with time and frequency, and with its position on or around the sun. We are also keenly interested in the *polarization* of the signal, for this is an important clue to its origin. In the sections that follow we shall describe the kinds of instruments that are used for determining these important parameters.

THE SIMPLE RADIO TELESCOPE

Figure 3-1 is a diagram of the simplest kind of radio telescope, which consists of a single antenna connected by a transmission

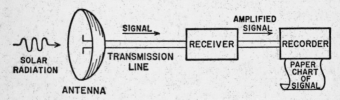

FIG. 3-1 The basic elements of a simple radio telescope. The antenna shown here is a parabolic dish that concentrates energy on a dipole placed at its focus.

line to a receiver. The amplified output signal from the receiver is fed into a recorder, where a permanent record is made, most often by a pen writing on a moving paper chart. For reasons that we shall discuss in the next chapter, provision is generally made for temporarily switching a calibrating signal into the receiver in place of the signal from the antenna. Such instruments have been widely used in certain areas of solar research. The fact that we have called them "simple" does not necessarily mean that they are *cheap*—the antenna might be a giant paraboloid costing millions of dollars!

The nature of the antenna varies widely, depending largely on the frequency that is to be received. In the microwave region of the radio spectrum the antenna is usually a parabolic reflector or "dish" that concentrates energy on a small receiving element placed at its focal point. At longer wavelengths the antenna may be a *yagi*, consisting of several parallel rods mounted on a common boom (fringe-area television antennas are commonly based on this design). In some instances radio astronomers use an array of dipoles, or elementary antennas, supported on fixed masts. While such an antenna can be made very large at relatively low cost, it has the obvious disadvantage that it cannot be mechanically "steered" to track a celestial target across the sky.

The antennas used in solar radio astronomy generally have high *directivity*—that is, they are effective in receiving signals only when they are aimed very nearly at the source. As such an antenna is rotated away from the source, the received power falls off sharply in the manner shown in Fig. 3-2. Directivity is

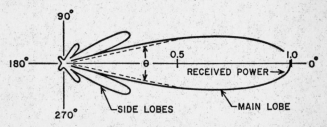

FIG. 3-2 Polar plot of the relative power received by a directional antenna as it is rotated through 360° in the presence of a distant point source. The main lobe is often referred to as the "beam" of the antenna.

usually measured by the angle θ, within which the received power exceeds half of its maximum value. This angle is known as the *beamwidth* of the antenna. Real antennas unfortunately tend to display secondary peaks in their directional patterns, producing the so-called *side lobes* shown in the figure. These lobes are quite analogous to the diffraction fringes that surround optical images, but in the radio case they occur on a much grosser scale because the wavelength of the radiation is larger relative to the aperture of the instrument. Many an unwary radio astronomer has been deceived into believing he had detected a weak source in the direction of his main lobe when the signal was actually that of a much stronger source in a side lobe.

There is an excellent analogy between a parabolic dish and the reflecting telescope that is used so widely in optical astronomy; in fact, the famous 200-in. telescope at Mount Palomar has actually been employed for millimeter-wavelength radio astronomy. Nevertheless, the reader should understand that a radio telescope does not provide a direct, visual image of a source. The radio telescope is like an optical telescope that is used solely to focus light on a photocell. An "image" of the source can be built up only by scanning the instrument back and forth and making a two-dimensional plot of the measured intensity as the telescope is pointed at different regions of the source; such an image is analogous to a contour map of geographical terrain, in which the stronger areas of the source stand out as "mountains." A picture of the sun obtained in this way is shown in Fig. 3-8.

It is obvious that such scanning can be effective only if the beamwidth of the radio telescope is much less than the angular width of the source. In optical language, the source must be *resolved.* Students of physics learn that the angular resolving power of an optical telescope depends upon the ratio of the wavelength of light to the diameter of the objective lens. The beamwidth of a radio telescope is given by a completely analogous expression,

$$\theta = \frac{\lambda}{L} \quad \text{rad} \quad \text{or} \quad \theta \cong 57 \, \frac{\lambda}{L} \quad \text{degrees,} \qquad (3\text{-}1)$$

where L is the effective width of the antenna in the plane in which θ is measured and λ is the operating wavelength expressed in the same units as L. In the case of a parabolic dish, L is approximately equal to the diameter of the dish. The reader should be warned that in either the optical or the radio case, calculations of resolving power are at best approximations. Resolution is not something that occurs abruptly just as the size of the instrument reaches the "magic" value given by Eq. (3-1). Furthermore, the theoretical resolution of an instrument is an ideal that is often not achieved in practice because of imperfections in design or construction.

How large must an antenna be to resolve the disc of the sun? If we let $\theta = \frac{1}{2}°$ in Eq. (3-1), we find that $L = 114\lambda$. Thus, at a wavelength of 1 cm a dish must be about 1.14 m in diameter if its beamwidth is to equal the apparent diameter of the sun. In order to scan the sun effectively, the dish should be perhaps 10 times this size, or some 38 ft in diameter. This figure is not too alarming, but if we increase the operating wavelength to 1 m, the required aperture becomes four times that of the largest dish in the world! We have already encountered the most serious problem in radio astronomy—that of achieving sufficient resolving power at a cost that is not too large a fraction of the national budget. In many applications, it is this problem that has led to the replacement of the simple radio telescope by the more sophisticated instruments described in the following sections.

ONE-DIMENSIONAL INTERFEROMETERS

To enjoy the full resolving power of an optical telescope it is not strictly necessary to use the entire area of the objective lens. Suppose we cover the lens with an opaque disc that has two small holes drilled in it near the ends of a diameter, as in Fig. 3-3(a). If we are looking at a circular object, the resolving power

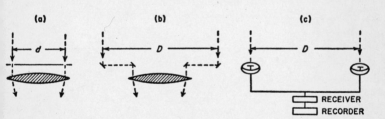

FIG. 3-3 Analogy between the radio interferometer and Michelson's stellar interferometer.

in one plane remains the same as if we were using an unobstructed lens whose diameter is equal to d, the distance between the holes. To be sure, there is an enormous loss of light, and the interpretation of the image is complicated by greatly increased effects of interference and diffraction. In fact, the image is no longer a simple disc, but a series of bright and dark interference fringes. In 1920 the American physicist Albert Michelson developed a *stellar interferometer* in which the holes of Fig. 3-3(a) were in effect moved farther apart by the system of four small mirrors shown in Fig. 3-3(b), thus giving the instrument the much greater resolving power of a telescope of aperture D. With this device attached to the historic 100-in. telescope at Mount Wilson, Michelson and F. G. Pease were actually able to measure the diameters of some of the larger of the nearby stars, a feat never before accomplished.[1]

Shortly after World War II it was realized that the principle of the stellar interferometer might be applied to the problem of resolution in radio astronomy which, as we have just seen, is a most serious one indeed. If two widely separated antennas are joined to a common receiver, as in Fig. 3-3(c), the resolution of the system equals that of a single very large antenna whose overall size is the same as the distance D between the two antennas. Of course, the energy-collecting capacity of the interferometer is merely that of the two small antennas, and once more we must pay a stiff price in increased complexity of interpretation. In the optical interferometer the simple image of a disc was transformed into a pattern of fringes. Similarly, in the radio interferometer the "image" or signal of a source becomes a series of fringes rather than a single well-defined peak.

What, exactly, does the signal of the sun look like in such an instrument? If the sun radiates steadily as it moves across the sky, the radio interferometer will record a set of fringes that look very much like the interference fringes produced in Young's experiment by light that strikes a screen after passing through a pair of narrow slits [Fig. 3-4(a)]. The two cases are actually quite similar, as we can see by referring to Fig. 3-4(b), which shows a solar radio wave incident on an interferometer at a time when the sun is β degrees from the vertical axis of the instrument. Let us assume that the transmission lines l_1 and l_2 are equal in length. Then if $D \sin \beta$ is an integral number of wavelengths, the signals from the two antennas a_1 and a_2 will be in phase

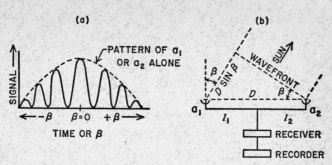

FIG. 3-4 Generation of fringe pattern in a two-element interferometer: (a) Pen record produced by passage of a small, steady source over the interferometer; (b) Geometry of the interferometer. [If the dashed envelope in (a) were plotted to the same scale as the fringe pattern, it would have only half the amplitude of the fringes themselves, since it represents the contribution of one antenna alone.]

when they combine at the receiver, and they will reinforce each other. The condition for a maximum signal, corresponding to the peak of a fringe, is thus

$$D \sin \beta = n\lambda, \quad \text{or} \quad \sin \beta = \frac{n\lambda}{D}, \tag{3-2}$$

where n is an integer. Each time the sun moves to a new position such that β satisfies this condition, another fringe is formed. On the other hand, when $D \sin \beta$ is an odd multiple of $\lambda/2$ the signals from a_1 and a_2 cancel each other and a null occurs in the fringe pattern.

In the idealized pen record of Fig. 3-4(a), the dashed envelope represents the directional pattern of the main lobe of either antenna if it were used alone. We have assumed that the two antennas are fixed; naturally, when the sun has drifted out of the individual antenna beams both the signals fall to zero and no further interference fringes can be generated. The effect of combining the two antennas has been to divide the rather broad beam of a single antenna into a number of much sharper fan-shaped lobes, each of which can now be used as a high-resolution probe for revealing detail or for determining position.

This important principle is further illustrated in Figs. 3-5(a) and 3-5(b), where we see sketches and conventional polar diagrams of the solid beam of a single antenna as well as the di-

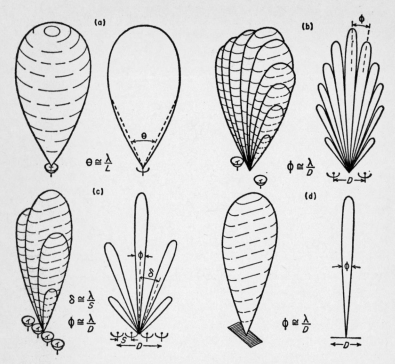

FIG. 3-5 Antenna patterns: (a) Single antenna of diameter *L*; (b) two-element interferometer with baseline *D*; (c) multi-element grating interferometer; (d) limiting case of grating. In each case the interferometer baseline *D* would normally run east-west.

vided beam of an interferometer. Notice in Fig. 3-5(b) that increased resolution is realized only in a plane containing the baseline between the two antennas; in a plane perpendicular to this, the resolution is no greater than that of either antenna alone. It is for this reason that interferometer baselines generally run east-west, so that the interference lobes scan across celestial sources as the earth rotates—or, from a more geocentric point of view, we can say that the sources "drift through" the lobes as the sky rotates from east to west. For observations of the sun this natural scanning rate of 15° per hour is often much too slow to delineate rapidly occurring events, and solar interferometers sometimes include a fast scan introduced by periodically varying the length of one of the transmission lines. In many interferometers the fall-off in fringe intensity on either side of $\beta = 0$ [Fig. 3-4(a)] is avoided by having the individual antennas track the sun across the sky, so that effective observations are possible throughout the day.

The principal price that we pay for the higher resolution of the interferometer is a certain degree of ambiguity, for when we detect a signal, it may have come from a source in any one of the many lobes of Fig. 3-5(b). The situation is rather like that of the executive who has a desk full of telephones and can't tell which one is ringing. Somewhat with tongue in cheek, radio astronomers categorize such problems under the general heading of "confusion"! Fortunately for our immediate problem, the sun is such a powerful emitter that we are not apt to be deceived by extraneous sources picked up in other lobes.

Thus far in our discussion of the interferometer we have assumed that the source is small compared with the angular spacing ϕ between lobes. What happens if the source is so extended that it occupies a number of lobes? In this event there is little change in the signal as the source drifts through the interference pattern and the fringes of Fig. 3-4(a) disappear. We say that the *fringe visibility* has dropped to zero. If the source is of intermediate size, perhaps comparable to ϕ, the amplitude of the fringes is decreased, but not to zero. Thus, fringe visibility is an important clue to the size of the source, especially if we can measure it with a variety of interferometer baselines.

Instead of using a single pair of antennas situated at opposite ends of a baseline, we might space a much larger number of antennas all along this same line. In optics this would be equivalent to replacing the two slits of Young's experiment with multiple slits or, in other words, with a diffraction grating. The effect of the additional elements is to suppress many of the interference lobes of Fig. 3-5(b), although the widths of the remaining lobes are the same as before [Fig. 3-5(c)]. If the total number of antennas in such a *grating interferometer* is n, the spacing between lobes will be about n times the width of a single lobe. With a pattern of this kind there is obviously less chance of confusion arising from secondary sources in "unused" lobes. It is not difficult to design a grating array with a lobe spacing large enough so that only one lobe at a time can fall on the sun, and a number of successful solar interferometers have been based on this principle.

If we further increase the number of individual antennas, so that n approaches infinity, we can think of the lobe spacing as having increased to the point where only one vertical fan remains, as in Fig. 3-5(d). In effect, we have gotten back to the case of a single large antenna. Such an array is admirably suited to studying galaxies, where we have a multitude of comparable sources sprinkled over the entire sky and the chances of confusion in a multi-lobe instrument are great. In the case of the sun, however, a single lobe is not necessarily an advantage, for now this lobe must somehow be made to track the sun if we are to obtain more than one brief glimpse each day.

Another useful trick (which seems to have no optical counterpart) is that of *lobe-switching*. If we add an extra half-wavelength of cable to one of the transmission lines l_1 or l_2 in Fig. 3-4(b), the fringe pattern will be shifted so that peaks occur where nulls used to be. By electrically switching the extra length of cable in and out of the circuit at a rapid rate, we can cause the fringes to scan back and forth between two adjacent regions of the sky. Now suppose that one of these regions contains a localized radio source, such as the sun. On one half of the switching cycle the instrument will "see" the source, while on the other half-cycle it will not. Thus the interferometer will generate an alternating signal that is readily detected and amplified by a proper receiver. On the other hand, a broad source like the background radio noise from the Milky Way gives rise to little or no signal, since the instrument sees virtually the same intensity for both fringe positions. The lobe-switching interferometer is highly effective in picking small sources out of background interference, and it also has the advantage of reducing problems of receiver noise and instability.

TWO-DIMENSIONAL INTERFEROMETERS

We have seen that a linear interferometer increases resolution in only one direction, normally east-west. This limitation can be overcome by properly combining the signals from *two* linear arrays, one of which extends east-west and the other north-south. Often the two lines of antennas are arranged in the form of a cross. The resulting antenna pattern can be visualized by imagining the superposition of two sets of fan beams like those of Fig. 3-5(c), with one set rotated 90° about a vertical axis. The regions of overlap of the two sets of fans define the interference lobes of the combination, giving rise to a series of diverging *pencil beams*. An array of this type is sometimes referred to as a "Chriscross," after its inventor W. N. Christiansen.[2]

If the number of individual antennas in the arms of the cross is made very large, so that each arm generates a single fan beam, as described in the preceding section, then only one pencil beam is produced where the two fans overlap. Because this arrangement was perfected by the Australian B. Y. Mills, it is known as a *Mills Cross*.[3]

A crossed interferometer of optimum design is a very powerful and relatively inexpensive instrument, for its resolution approximates that of a dish whose diameter equals the length of one arm of the cross. Of course, the energy-gathering area of the cross is vastly less than that of the equivalent dish, and its beam can be "steered" only with difficulty by a complex process of electrically phasing the signals from the individual antennas. The success of the two-dimensional interferometer is indicated by the fact that a number of large instruments of this type are now under construction. Crosses with arms 1 km long are being built in Italy and in the Soviet Union, while a huge cross recently completed in Australia has arms that are a full mile in length![4]

SOLAR RADIO SPECTROGRAPHS

In Chapter 5 we shall see that solar radio outbursts often span an enormous range of frequencies. All across this wide spectrum changes occur with bewildering rapidity on a time scale that may be measured in seconds. There is no time for a leisurely, point-by-point exploration of the spectrum; what is needed is an instrument that will provide an instantaneous, panoramic view of the entire gamut of frequencies, and it is the function of the *radio spectrograph* to meet this demand.

The heart of a radio spectrograph is a swept-frequency receiver—that is, a receiver which is repeatedly tuned across the same wide band of frequencies by a mechanical or electrical device that generally produces several frequency sweeps per second. Equally important is an antenna whose response is nearly constant over this same range. Finally, the output of the receiver must be displayed in such a way as to provide a permanent record of solar intensity versus frequency at each moment of time. This is usually accomplished by allowing the signal from the receiver to control the brightness of the luminous spot on a cathode-ray tube. The spot is swept across the face of the tube in exact synchronism with the tuning of the receiver, producing a trace of varying brightness that is, in effect, the desired plot of radio intensity versus frequency. Each frequency sweep generates a new trace, and the successive traces are recorded photographically on a film that moves slowly and continuously in a direction perpendicular to the motion of the spot. It is this mechanical movement of the film that establishes the time scale of the resulting record. Plate XIII is an example of a recording made in this manner; note that in this instance the motion of the spot was in the vertical direction, while the film moved from right to left. Such a record of signal intensity in the time-frequency domain is often referred to as a *dynamic spectrum*.

Because it is difficult to get a single receiver-antenna combination to operate successfully over a frequency range of more than two to one, an elaborate radio spectrograph may consist of several such units, each covering a different portion of the total range of the instrument. It is indeed fortunate that the sun is such a strong source, for the requirements of great bandwidth and rapid scanning are fundamentally incompatible with high sensitivity.

The principles of the interferometer and the radio spectrograph have been combined in the *swept-frequency interferometer*. Whereas the ordinary interferometer is a powerful device for measuring the position of a source at a single frequency, the swept-frequency instrument can provide positional data as a function of frequency as well as of time. Instruments of this type have proven to be of great utility in following rapidly moving, broadband disturbances in the sun's atmosphere.[5]

THE MEASUREMENT OF POLARIZATION

Although the topic of polarization leads to conceptual and experimental complexities, one cannot well avoid it, for the polarization of an electromagnetic wave often carries an important message regarding the way in which the wave was generated and the kind of medium through which it has passed. We learn in optics that when we talk about the polarization of a wave we are attempting to describe the detailed manner in which the electromagnetic field is vibrating. Figure 3-6 shows stylized repre-

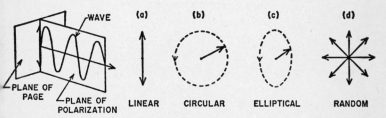

FIG. 3-6 Types of polarization. The sketch at the left illustrates how the stylized representation at (a) is generated as a linearly polarized sinusoidal electric wave moves out of the page.

sentations of the several kinds of polarization with which we are concerned. In each case the reader should imagine that the wave is coming toward him out of the plane of the paper, and that the arrows depict the direction of the electric field in this plane as the wave flows out of the page. This kind of representation gives the best feeling for the electrical driving forces that will be experienced by an antenna as such a wave moves past it.

The simplest kind of wave is one that is *linearly polarized*. In this case the vibrations of the electric field are confined to a single plane that contains the direction of propagation, as in the sketch at the left of Fig. 3-6. Such waves are also said to be "plane polarized." In Fig. 3-6(a), the reader should visualize the electric field in the plane of the page as vibrating up and down, with a sinusoidally varying intensity. Most radio antennas transmit or receive waves of this type; if an incident wave is of a more complex variety, an ordinary receiving antenna will automatically sort out the appropriate linear component of the wave.

Figure 3-6(b) shows a *circularly polarized* wave. Here the electric vector is of constant amplitude, but it rotates in the plane of the page as the wave moves forward. If the vector rotates in the direction shown, the wave is said to be circularly polarized in the "right-hand" sense, but if the direction of rotation is reversed, the polarization is described as "left-hand." For an *elliptically polarized* wave, the electric vector again rotates in the plane of the page, but its amplitude varies in such a way that the tip of the vector traces out an ellipse. The convention of right- or left-handedness is used in the same sense as for circular polarization.

Figure 3-6(d) is a crude representation of a *randomly polarized* wave, which consists of a superposition of all possible planes of linear polarization, with randomly varying circular and elliptical components thrown in for good measure. It may seem strange that this kind of wave, which is the most complex of all, is by far the most common in nature, and that it is often called "unpolarized" when in fact it is a mixture of *all* polarizations!

How do we measure the polarization of a radio wave? The common types of antennas are themselves linearly polarized, in the sense that they respond only to those components of electrical vibrations that are parallel to their elements. If we are dealing with a linearly polarized wave, we can readily determine its plane of polarization by rotating such an antenna about an axis perpendicular to its elements and noting the orientation for which a maximum signal is received. This is rather analogous to determining the direction of polarization of plane-polarized light by rotating a piece of Polaroid material. If the radio wave is known to be circularly polarized, we can measure its sense of rotation by mounting two simple antennas at right angles to each other and combining their outputs after one of the signals has been retarded by an extra quarter-wavelength of cable. Depending upon which signal is so delayed, the system will respond either to right-hand or to left-hand waves. The optical analog of this experiment is the quarter-wave plate.

In order to specify the polarization completely in the general case, we must determine four quantities—the so-called *Stokes parameters*.[6] If the source is a steady emitter, so that ample time is available, the necessary measurements can be made with an interferometer whose antennas are physically rotated during the investigation. For a rapidly changing source like the sun, two sets of mutually perpendicular antennas are generally used, with electronic switching to permit rapid combination of the signals in the proper sequence to determine the necessary parameters.[7]

SOME EXAMPLES OF SOLAR RADIO TELESCOPES

We have been discussing the general principles on which solar radio telescopes operate. Now we are going to look in somewhat more detail at several actual examples of such instruments. Our examples were chosen, not necessarily because they are the "biggest" or the "best," or even the "first," but because they illustrate certain of the principles about which we have been talking, and because information about them is readily available.

A Simple Radio Telescope. A parabolic radio telescope 10 ft in diameter may not seem very impressive when we hear almost daily of giant dishes with apertures ranging up to 1000 ft. Nevertheless, a 10-ft reflector can be a productive research tool if its surface is accurate enough to be used at very short wavelengths (the usual rule-of-thumb is that the surface errors must not exceed $\frac{1}{20}$ of a wavelength).

In 1956 the U.S. Naval Research Laboratory began a study of the sun with a 10-ft paraboloid that had been machined from a single aluminum casting with such precision that it could be used at the unusually short wavelength of 4.3 mm.[8] The dish was mounted on a radar pedestal tipped so that one axis pointed at the Pole Star to produce what astronomers term an *equatorial mounting*. With this arrangement the sun (or any other celestial source) can be followed by rotating the instrument about a single axis. A small horn was located at the focal point of the paraboloid to receive the reflected signal, which was then conducted through waveguide to a special low-noise receiver at the back of the dish.

In practice, the antenna was pointed slightly ahead of the sun with the aid of an optical sighting telescope. The mounting was locked in this position and the output of the receiver was recorded as the sun drifted through the stationary beam of the radio telescope. This procedure was repeated over and over during a day's observations in order to obtain a large number of scans of the solar surface. Figure 3-7 shows a typical scan

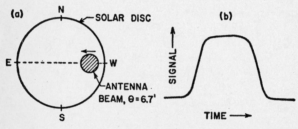

FIG. 3-7 (a) Beam of 10-ft radio telescope compared with solar disc; (b) record of a typical scan across the undisturbed sun on February 18, 1957. The operating wavelength is 4.3 mm. (After R. J. Coates.[8])

beside a comparison of the antenna beamwidth with the solar disc. From these data the radio brightness distribution across the sun could be determined, as well as the apparent diameter and temperature of the solar surface. Minor effects due to active regions were identified on some of the records, although we shall see that the disturbed sun is not as spectacular in the millimeter region as it is at longer wavelengths.

A Two-dimensional Solar Interferometer. In the preceding section we found that a single 10-ft dish can be useful for solar research. Stanford University has assembled no less than 32 paraboloids of this size in the form of a crossed interferometer that is used on a regular basis for mapping the brightness of the sun's surface at a wavelength of 9.1 cm.[9] This instrument, known as a *microwave spectroheliograph,* is shown in Plate XI. The reader should have no difficulty in identifying the basic design as that of the Christiansen cross.

Each arm of the cross is composed of 16 equatorially mounted dishes equally spaced along a 375-ft baseline. A single one-horse-power motor drives all of the antennas in unison to track the sun as it crosses the sky from east to west. In the notation used in Fig. 3-5, the beamwidth θ of a single paraboloid is 2.3°, while the half-power width ϕ of one of the pencil beams of the interference pattern is only 3.1'. The instrument was designed for a lobe spacing δ of 41' in order to guarantee that only one beam at a time can fall on the sun. As the sun moves through the pattern it is scanned from west to east by a new pencil beam approximately every three minutes, so that little observing time is wasted between scans. In order to produce a two-dimensional map, the successive scans are progressively shifted in the north-south direction by automatic phasing devices in the corresponding arm of the cross. The result is that in less than an hour the entire face of the sun has been covered by about 15 parallel scan lines, much like the pattern of a television picture. Figure 3-8 shows an actual radio map of the sun produced in this manner; immediately below the map is one of the individual scans from which it was synthesized.

A Solar Radio Spectrograph. Because a swept-frequency receiver is by its very nature vulnerable to man-made interference, Harvard University elected to locate its solar radio spectrograph in an isolated mountain valley in western Texas.[10] The Fort Davis Radio Astronomy Station, as it is called, operates a total of six swept-frequency receivers, which cover the ranges 25-50, 50-100, 100-180, 180-320, 320-580, and 2100-3900 Mc/sec. Signals for the two low-frequency channels are provided by broad-band "bow-tie" dipole antennas mounted above a reflecting screen. Plate XII shows the equatorially mounted 28-ft paraboloid that supplies signals to the four high-frequency receivers, each of which has its own "feed" dipole or horn mounted near the focal point of the dish to collect its share of the focused solar energy. As its daily chore the antenna automatically tracks the sun from sunrise to sunset.

Each of the receivers sweeps through its band three times per second, and the signals are displayed on six cathode-ray tubes mounted in a vertical line. A camera photographs all six traces

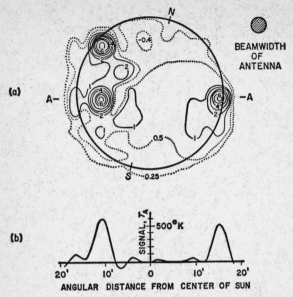

FIG. 3-8 (a) Map of the sun made by the Stanford microwave spectroheliograph. The heavy circle outlines the visible disc, while the contours represent the *radio brightness temperature* in units of 70,000° K; (b) pencil-beam scan of the sun along the line AA. The ordinate is *antenna temperature*, T_A. Brightness temperature and antenna temperature are defined in Chapter 4. (After R. N. Bracewell and G. Swarup[9])

on a single 70-mm motion-picture film that moves continuously at a speed of 12 mm per minute. Plate XIII is an example of a recording made in this manner. The Fort Davis spectrograph has been operated on a daily basis since 1956, although the last of the six receivers was not completed until 1960.

With an instrument such as this, no attempt is made to scan the sun, or to localize sources of radiation on its surface. Indeed, by applying Eq. (3-1), the reader can quickly show that over virtually all of its frequency range the 28-ft antenna "sees" the sun merely as an unresolved point source.

An Orbital Radio Observatory. The wave of the future was foreshadowed during 1964 by the launching of an artificial satellite carrying a solar radio telescope. This instrument was one of 20 experiments that rode into space aboard an Orbiting Geophysical Observatory, commonly known as "OGO." Launched from Florida's Cape Kennedy by an Atlas-Agena rocket, OGO followed an eccentric orbit that took it as far as 93,000 miles from the earth's surface. At perigee, or closest approach, the complex satellite was at an altitude of only 175 miles.

The radio-astronomical experiment was designed by Dr. F. T. Haddock of the University of Michigan, an institution with a long history of important contributions to solar research. Basically, the instrument was a swept-frequency receiver covering the range from 2 to 4 Mc/sec. Signals were to be supplied by an antenna in the form of a long metal ribbon that was coiled on a reel during the launching operation and then unwound into space after the satellite had achieved orbit. OGO had extensive "on-board" facilities for recording and storing data on magnetic tape for later transmission to ground stations. The original plan called for the spacecraft to be stabilized with one face always pointed at the earth, but a malfunction prevented this maneuver and left OGO tumbling through space. Even worse, the solar antenna failed to unfurl properly. While the first orbital solar radio telescope experienced the kind of difficulties that are apt to plague any pioneering effort, there is little doubt that such experiments will be continued and that vitally important observations of the sun's radio spectrum will be made from space vehicles within the next few years.

Why should anyone wish to undertake the difficult and costly task of making radio measurements from space? Fundamentally, the answer lies in the earth's ionosphere, a thick spherical shell of electrons and positive ions that surrounds our globe at altitudes ranging from 60 to 600 km. The ionosphere is a great boon to radio engineers, for it acts much like a metallic mirror, bouncing their signals back to the ground and making it possible to communicate over long distances around the curve of the earth's surface. By the same token, it is a curse to radio astronomers, since it reflects signals from celestial sources back into space and forever prevents them from reaching ground-based radio telescopes.

Fortunately for the astronomer, the ionosphere shows its mirror-like behavior only for radio waves whose frequency lies below a certain *critical frequency* f_0. Waves of higher frequency readily penetrate the ionized layers, at least if they arrive from sources near the zenith. If we let N represent the electron density, or number of electrons per cubic centimeter, in the densest region of the ionosphere, then

$$f_0 = e \sqrt{\frac{N}{\pi m}} \text{ cps,} \tag{3-3}$$

or

$$f_0 \cong 9 \times 10^{-3} \sqrt{N} \text{ Mc/sec.} \tag{3-4}$$

Here e is the charge of the electron in electrostatic units, while m is its mass in grams. Since the electron density is largely controlled by solar radiation, f_0 increases sharply during the day and during the years near sunspot maximum.

Speaking in general terms, radio astronomers are seldom seriously bothered by the ionosphere as long as they work at frequencies above 20 Mc/sec. Below this frequency the problem becomes increasingly annoying until, even under the most favorable conditions, a lower limit to useful observations is reached near 5 Mc/sec. At these low frequencies the ionosphere not only attenuates the incoming signals—it also reflects into the upward-looking antennas an overwhelming din of interference from radio stations and distant thunderstorms. If reliable observations are needed at still lower frequencies, the only recourse is to place our instruments in a satellite well above the troublesome ionosphere. Looking somewhat further into the future, the most satisfactory solution of all may be the establishment of permanent radio observatories on the moon. If our natural satellite has any ionosphere at all, it is so highly rarefied as to present no problem to radio astronomers.

The reader may well ask why one should be so stubborn as to insist on working in the troublesome region below 20 Mc/sec, which is, after all, only a small part of the total radio spectrum. This is somewhat like asking a low-temperature physicist why he should spend years of his life and large sums of money studying the last degree on the Kelvin scale! In each case the answer is that these limited regions are teeming with intriguing scientific phenomena. For example, almost all of the energy of Jupiter's mysterious and powerful radio outbursts is concentrated in the regions below 20 Mc/sec; some of the strongest solar bursts occur here, and important changes take place in the radio spectra of the Milky Way and the radio galaxies. It seems inevitable that an important facet of the exploration of space will be the making of radio-astronomical observations from beyond the earth's ionosphere.

AMATEUR OBSERVATIONS OF THE RADIO SUN

The disturbed sun is the easiest celestial source to observe with simple radio equipment. An ordinary short-wave receiver is quite capable of detecting strong solar outbursts if it is connected to a suitable antenna. Because proper identification of suspected signals is a major problem, the chances of success are enhanced if the antenna has fairly high directivity and can be pointed at the sun. The three-element "beam" antenna often used by "hams" is well adapted to this use, especially if it is mounted so that it can be tilted upward.

Since we are looking for outbursts from the *disturbed* sun, our observations are most likely to succeed if they are made during known periods of solar activity. A large group of sunspots near the center of the sun's disc is a favorable omen that can be recognized with a small optical telescope, or even a pair of binoculars. However, the reader is sternly admonished never to look at the sun with *any* optical instrument unless the light has been reduced to a safe level by filters that are known to be adequate. By far the safest method of all is to project the solar image on a white card held a few inches behind the eyepiece.

The radio receiver should be tuned to a frequency high enough so that interference from stations is not troublesome—perhaps somewhere in the vicinity of 20 Mc/sec—and the volume should be increased until the steady hiss of background noise is heard. Depending upon the quality of the receiver, this noise may be largely internal, but hopefully most of it will be due to the ever-present signal from our Milky Way. In the latter case the noise should drop sharply if we disconnect the antenna.

The sound that we are listening for is a rapid increase in the

hissing noise, succeeded by a smooth decline to the original
level, often following the rather typical form of the events shown
in Fig. 3-9. If a signal is suspected of being station interference

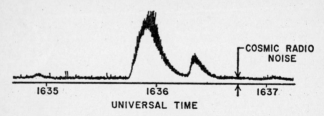

FIG. 3-9 Several Type III bursts recorded at 22 Mc/sec at the University of Florida's
southern hemisphere station near Maipu, Chile. This 3-minute sample is typical of
dozens of such bursts that accompanied a large flare on April 2, 1960. Notice that
the bursts are superimposed on a steady signal due to the "cosmic radio noise"
from our Milky Way galaxy. Chapter 5 describes other types of bursts that might
be detected.

it can quickly be identified by a slight retuning of the receiver,
which will eliminate a station but not the broad-band solar noise.
The other common form of interference is static generated by
distant lightning, which produces a brief crashing sound easily
distinguished from the far slower rise and fall of a solar burst.
An important advantage of a "steerable" antenna is that it can
alternately be swung toward and away from the sun as an aid
to identification during periods of suspicious noise. If the experimenter can command some means, such as a simple pen recorder, of making a permanent record of his observations, he is
strongly urged to do so. He is also reminded that listening for
solar bursts is a good deal like fishing—it may require more
than a little patience!

During the next few years solar activity will once more be
rising toward a new crescendo, with another sunspot maximum
expected around 1968. These will be opportune years for solar
observations of every kind.

REFERENCES

1. Twiss, R. Q., "Physical Principles of Stellar Interferometers," in
   Space Physics and Radio Astronomy, edited by H. Messel and S. T.
   Butler (The Macmillan Co., London, 1964).

2. Christiansen, W. N. and Mathewson, D. S., "Scanning the Sun with a Highly Directional Array," Proc. Inst. Radio Engrs. 46, 127-131 (1958).

3. Mills, B. Y., "Cross-type Radio Telescopes," Proc. Inst. Radio Engrs. Australia 24, 132-140 (1963).

4. Mills, B. Y., Aitchison, R. E., Little, A. G., and McAdam, W. B., "The Sydney University Cross-type Radio Telescope," Proc. Inst. Radio Engrs. Australia 24, 156-165 (1963).

5. Sheridan, K. V., "Techniques for the Investigation of Solar Radio Bursts at Metre Wavelengths," Proc. Inst. Radio Engrs. Australia 24, 174-184 (1963).

6. Shurcliff, W. A. and Ballard, S. S., *Polarized Light* (Momentum Book No. 7, D. Van Nostrand Co. Inc., Princeton, 1964), pp. 76-80.

7. Cohen, M. H., "Radio Astronomy Polarization Measurements," Proc. Inst. Radio Engrs. 46, 174-183 (1958).

8. Coates, R. J., "Measurements of Solar Radiation and Atmospheric Attenuation at 4.3-Millimeters Wavelength," Proc. Inst. Radio Engrs. 46, 122-126 (1958).

9. Bracewell, R. N. and Swarup, G., "The Stanford Microwave Spectroheliograph Antenna, A Microsteradian Pencil-Beam Interferometer," *I.R.E.* Trans. Antennas Propagation **AP9**, 22-30 (1961).

10. Thompson, A. R., "Spectral Observations of Solar Radio Bursts I. Receiving Equipment," Astrophys. J. 133, 643-648 (1961).

FOR FURTHER READING

Bolton, J. G., "Radio Telescopes," in *Telescopes,* edited by G. P. Kuiper and B. M. Middlehurst (University of Chicago Press, Chicago, 1960).

Bracewell, R. N., "Radio Astronomy Techniques," in *Handbuch der Physik,* Vol. 54, edited by S. Flugge (Springer-Verlag, Berlin, 1962), pp. 42-129.

Findlay, J. W., "Antennas and Receivers for Radio Astronomy," in *Advances in Radio Research,* Vol. 2, edited by J. A. Saxton (Academic Press Inc., New York, 1964), pp. 37-119.

Hanbury Brown, R. and Lovell, A. C. B., *The Exploration of Space by Radio* (Chapman and Hall Ltd., London, 1957), pp. 29-59.

Hyde, F. W., *Radio Astronomy for Amateurs* (W. W. Norton and Co., Inc., New York, 1963).

Steinberg, J. L. and Lequeux, J., *Radio Astronomy* (McGraw-Hill Book Co., Inc., New York, 1963), pp. 20-95.

4   *Radio Signals from the Quiet Sun*

*"I will sit down now, but the time will come
when you will hear me."*

DISRAELI

In the first chapter we saw how Southworth was led to discover the radio emission from the quiet sun. Perhaps "discover"
is too strong a word here, since Planck's theory clearly predicted
that any hot body should radiate a broad spectrum of energy,
some of which must inevitably extend into the radio region. By
1942 the observations of Southworth and King were more in the
nature of a further confirmation of this already well-established
theory.

BLACKBODY RADIATION

Because the radio emission of the quiet sun is thermal in
origin, our first task in the present chapter is to understand the
nature of such radiation, a topic usually discussed in terms of an
idealization known as a *blackbody*. What do we mean by this
rather curious term? A blackbody is an object that completely
absorbs all of the radiation that falls on it, so that none is reflected. In the visible spectrum a surface coated with soot approximates this ideal. According to a well-established principle
of physics known as *Kirchhoff's law,* a good absorber is also a
good emitter, and thus a blackbody is the most efficient kind of
thermal radiator. It is to a blackbody radiator that Planck's theory actually applies, providing an accurate description of the
way in which the emitted power varies with wavelength.

The solid line in Fig. 4-1 is the radiation curve for a blackbody

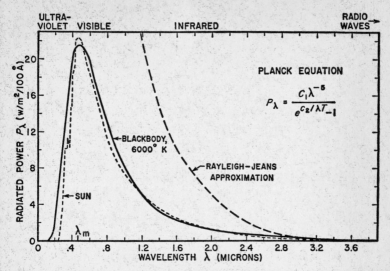

ULTRA-VIOLET VISIBLE INFRARED RADIO WAVES

PLANCK EQUATION

$$P_\lambda = \frac{c_1 \lambda^{-5}}{e^{c_2/\lambda T} - 1}$$

BLACKBODY, 6000° K

RAYLEIGH–JEANS APPROXIMATION

SUN

λ_m

FIG. 4-1 Radiation curves of the sun and a blackbody. The equation in the diagram is Planck's law, in which c_1 and c_2 are numerical constants. The dashed curve shows how the Rayleigh-Jeans approximation approaches Planck's law at long wavelengths.

at a temperature of 6000° K, as predicted by the Planck theory. Notice that the curve peaks in the visible part of the spectrum, and that it declines rather slowly and asymptotically toward the longer wavelengths. It is this long tail, extending into the radiofrequency region to the right of the diagram, that is of interest to radio astronomers. The observed radiation curve of the sun is shown in the figure as a dashed line. Perhaps we should be surprised that it fits the 6000° blackbody curve as well as it does, when we remember that solar radiation comes not from a single surface at a single temperature, but rather from a thick layer that spans a wide range of temperatures. Furthermore, the sun's radiation is subject to selective absorption as it emerges through the turbulent solar atmosphere.

What would happen to the blackbody curve of Fig. 4-1 if the temperature were something other than 6000°? If the temperature were to rise, the curve would everywhere increase in height and the peak would shift toward shorter wavelengths; if the temperature fell, the ordinates would all decrease and the peak would move to the right. In fact, the absolute temperature T and the wavelength of the peak, λ_m, are related by a simple expression known as *Wien's law:*

$$\lambda_m T = 2.897 \times 10^{-3} \text{ meter degrees.} \qquad (4\text{-}1)$$

Planck's equation has been reproduced in Fig. 4-1, and we see that it is quite cumbersome for computational purposes. Luckily for radio astronomers, there is a simpler formula, known as the *Rayleigh-Jeans law,* which gives almost the same results at the longer wavelengths. In the customary (and unavoidably awkward) units of radio astronomy, the Rayleigh-Jeans equation is

$$P_\lambda = \frac{2\pi k T}{\lambda^2} \text{ w/m}^2\text{/cps,} \qquad (4\text{-}2)$$

where k is the Boltzmann constant, which has a numerical value of 1.38×10^{-23}. Since this is an important law, we should be sure that we understand it clearly. P_λ is the power in watts emitted by one square meter of a blackbody surface whose temperature is T °K; this power is measured over a frequency band 1 cps wide centered on the wavelength λ, where λ is expressed in meters. Equation (4-2) tells us that in the radiofrequency region P_λ falls off with the inverse *square* of the wavelength. Little wonder, then, that radio astronomers make most of their measurements of thermal energy at very short wavelengths!

Let us apply the Rayleigh-Jeans law to see how much energy the sun should emit at a wavelength of, say, 1 m if we naively assume that it radiates like a blackbody at a temperature of 6000° K. Using Eq. (4-2), we find that P_λ has the surprisingly small value of 5.2×10^{-19} w/m²/cps. Of course, this is the power that is contained in a band only 1 cps wide; if we were to monitor the radiation with a receiver having the more realistic bandwidth of 10^6 cps, we would detect a million times more energy.

But wait! Equation (4-2) refers to the power per unit area emitted right at the surface of the sun. In Chapter 2 we found that by the time it reaches the earth, solar radiation has been attenuated by the factor $(R_0/d)^2$, where R_0 is the radius of the sun and d is the distance from the sun to the earth. The *re-*

ceived power per unit area, which radio astronomers call the flux density S, is therefore

$$S = \frac{2\pi k T}{\lambda^2}\left(\frac{R_0}{d}\right)^2 \text{ w/m}^2\text{/cps.} \qquad (4\text{-}3)$$

Since R_0/d is about 4.7×10^{-3}, our calculations now tell us that we should expect a flux density of only 1.1×10^{-23} w/m²/cps at our wavelength of 1 m. It is scarcely surprising that such estimates discouraged experimenters in the early days of radio!

The reader will already have sensed that in the practical case we can reverse the preceding calculation in order to determine the temperature of the source. That is, if we can measure S we can easily solve Eq. (4-3) for T. Of course, the total power P_T that is collected by a radio telescope is not directly equal to S, since S represents the flux incident on *unit* area. It is evident that $S = P_T/A$, where A is the effective collecting area of the antenna, and thus the measurement of S comes down to evaluating P_T and A.

P_T is commonly measured through the arrangement shown in Fig. 4-2. After the output signal due to P_T has been recorded,

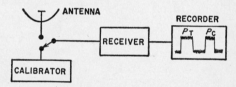

FIG. 4-2 Calibration of a radio telescope.

the receiver input is switched to a calibration circuit that provides a variable but known noise power P_C. When the calibrator level has been adjusted so that the receiver output equals that caused by the sun, then $P_T = P_C$.

What about the effective collecting area of the antenna? Even in the simplest cases, we may encounter gross errors if we merely assume that A is equal to the physical area of the antenna. The effective area of a parabolic dish, for example, is only about half of its actual area. We can estimate A from antenna theory, or it can be measured by using known natural or artificial sources. Since it is a factor that is difficult to assess with high precision, it is usually responsible for most of the uncertainty in calculating S and, therefore, the temperature of the source.

RADIO BRIGHTNESS

We have just seen that we can determine the temperature of a blackbody source by measuring S, the received flux density. However, in this calculation we had to know both the size and the distance of the object. Furthermore, if the source extends beyond the limits of the antenna beam—that is, if it is resolved —the mere measurement of flux density becomes rather meaningless, since no single antenna pointing can collect flux from the whole source. The concept of flux density is really appropriate only when the object is effectively a point source, a condition that is fulfilled by the sun when it is studied at low frequencies with a radio telescope of small aperture.

In order to deal with extended sources that are resolved by their instruments, radio astronomers introduce the idea of *brightness, b,* which is defined as flux density per unit solid angle. That is,

$$b \equiv \left(\frac{S}{\Omega}\right) \text{w/m}^2/\text{cps/sterad.} \qquad (4\text{-}4)$$

If the object is indeed resolved, the solid angle Ω from which flux is being received is determined by the beamwidth of the radio telescope. We can then scan the source with our antenna and map the distribution of brightness over its surface, as in Fig. 3-8. In this way we gain important new information about the structure of the source—information that cannot be obtained from a simple measurement of flux density with an instrument of low resolution.

We can extend the concept of brightness to an object that is not resolved, but in this event we must have prior knowledge of its angular size, since Ω is then defined by the source rather than by the instrument. Referring to Fig. 4-3, if A_0 is the cross-sectional area of the sun, then from the definition of a solid angle, $\Omega = A_0/d^2 = \pi R_0^2/d^2$ sterad. We can combine Eqs. (4-3) and (4-4) to obtain

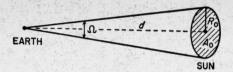

FIG. 4-3 Geometry of the solid angle subtended by the sun.

$$b = \frac{2kT}{\lambda^2} \text{ w/m}^2/\text{cps/sterad.} \qquad (4-5)$$

Obviously, if we can measure b we can use Eq. (4-5) to compute the corresponding temperature of the source on the assumption that we are dealing with blackbody radiation. A temperature calculated on this basis is appropriately called a *brightness temperature*, T_b. Evidently,

$$T_b \equiv \frac{b\lambda^2}{2k} \text{ °K.} \qquad (4-6)$$

Astronomers use the concept of brightness temperature freely, even though it may not be known whether the source in question behaves at all like a blackbody. Often it is used when the source is known *not* to be thermal! When we say that a source has a brightness temperature of 20,000° K at a certain wavelength, all we really mean is that its brightness is the same *as if* we were observing a blackbody surface at that temperature.

One of the attributes of brightness temperature is that it can be measured directly through an interesting property of antennas. Let us suppose that we have a radio telescope pointed toward an extended source, as in Fig. 4-4(a). The beamwidth θ is small enough so that the antenna sees only a limited area of the

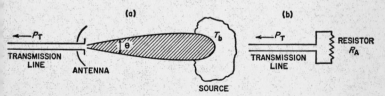

FIG. 4-4 Measurement of brightness temperature. In (a) the shaded area represents the main lobe of the antenna pattern.

source, for which the brightness temperature is T_b. We assume that as usual the antenna is "matched" to the transmission line —that is, that the effective resistance R_A of the antenna is equal to that of the line. Under these conditions the antenna will deliver to the transmission line a power $P_T = kT_b$ watts/cps. Now, we learn in electronics that any resistance generates a certain electrical noise of its own because of the random thermal motions of its electrons. If, in place of the antenna, we terminate our transmission line with a resistance of R_A ohms, as in Fig. 4-4(b), the noise power that the resistor feeds into the line is $P_T = kT$ watts/cps, where T is the temperature of the resistor. In other words, *the antenna generates the same signal as an equivalent resistance that is at the temperature of the surface at which the antenna is pointed.*

This simple fact provides the basis for a direct measurement of brightness temperature. First we point the radio telescope at the source and note the reading of the output meter. Next, the antenna is disconnected from the transmission line and replaced by an equivalent resistor, which is heated until the output meter reads the same as before. The temperature of the resistor, which can be measured by any of the usual methods, is then equal to T_b, the brightness temperature of the source. Strangely enough, we can determine the temperature of the sun, 93 million miles away, by measuring the temperature of a resistor in the laboratory! In actual practice the technique is complicated somewhat by the necessity of making corrections for the antenna pattern and for signal losses in the atmosphere and in the transmission line.

Because of the relationships just discussed, astronomers often speak of the *antenna temperature* T_A that is generated by a source. T_A has nothing whatever to do with the physical temperature of the antenna itself; it is simply the temperature to which the resistance R_A must be raised in order for its noise power to match the signal from the source. We have seen that when the source completely fills the antenna beam, T_A is equal to the brightness temperature T_b of the source. On the other hand, if the solid angle ω subtended by the source is less than the solid angle Ω occupied by the antenna beam, then $T_A = (\omega/\Omega)T_b$.

As the source approaches a point, ω/Ω becomes very small and T_A is only a tiny fraction of T_b.

THE MYSTERY OF THE SUN'S TEMPERATURE

In Chapter 1 we saw that Southworth and King made the first radio measurement of the sun's temperature at a wavelength of 3.2 cm. Thanks to an error in his calculations, Southworth at first believed that his work had merely confirmed the temperature of 6000° K that optical astronomers had long before established for the photosphere. When the mistake was corrected, however, the radio temperature jumped to 20,000° K, more than three times the accepted figure. What could be the reason for such a glaring discrepancy?

The mystery was unravelled in 1946 by the theoretical work of the Australian D. F. Martyn and the Russian V. L. Ginzburg. Using methods that had been developed for tracing radio waves through the earth's ionosphere, Martyn and Ginzburg showed that solar radio waves of different frequencies must originate at different levels in the sun's deep atmosphere. There was no longer any reason to be surprised because Southworth's measurements had failed to agree with the accepted temperature of the photosphere, for the energy that he received had not come from the photosphere at all, but from the chromosphere, which is far hotter. As is so often the case, disagreement had arisen because people were not really talking about the same thing! The theory indicates that as we listen at longer and longer wavelengths the signals that we hear should come from greater and greater altitudes in the solar atmosphere. Since the temperatures of the atmospheric layers increase with height, this means that we should see a sun that grows progressively hotter as our operating wavelength increases.

The predictions of Martyn and Ginzburg have been fully borne out by subsequent observations. Figure 4-5 shows the enormous change that takes place in the measured temperature of the sun as we move through the radio spectrum. At millimeter wavelengths T_d is not far from the traditional photospheric temperature of 6000° K, indicating that the radio signals must come

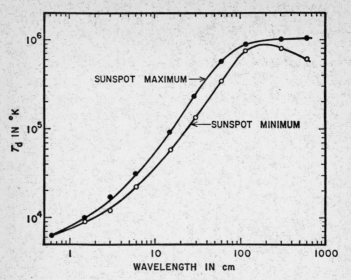

FIG. 4-5 Apparent temperature of the sun at various radio wavelengths. T_d is the *disc temperature*, an average brightness temperature calculated from Eqs. (4-4) and (4-5) on the assumption that the measured radio flux comes from a uniform disc the size of the photosphere. (Data from C. W. Allen.[1])

from nearly the same level as the visible radiation. In the centimeter range T_d rises to values typical of the chromosphere, implying that the radio emission is now centered in that turbulent region. Finally, the meter wavelengths seem to share the million-degree temperature of the corona, leading us to believe that the lower radiofrequencies arise in the thin gases of the sun's outer envelope. Clearly the radio astronomer has in his hands a powerful tool; merely by varying the operating wavelength of his radio telescope he can make a layer-by-layer analysis of the solar atmosphere, much like an archaeologist uncovering level upon level of history with his shovel. Like the archaeologist, however, the astronomer still has some challenging problems of interpretation!

THE EFFECTIVE RADIATION LEVEL

Why is it that solar radio waves of a given frequency f originate almost entirely in a thin layer of gas at a definite height h_e

above the photosphere? To give a complete answer, we must first explain why energy of this frequency does not come from *above* h_c, and then why it cannot come from *below* h_c. Our answers to these twin questions will give us a useful insight into the important problem of how radio waves are generated and propagated in an ionized gas such as the solar atmosphere.

The fact that little radiation is born in the comparatively thin and transparent regions above h_c (Fig. 4-6) is a consequence of

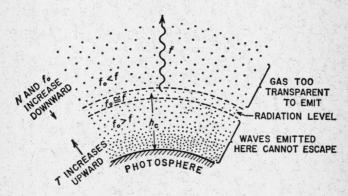

FIG. 4-6 The effective radiation level h_c in the solar atmosphere. N is the local electron density, f_0 is the local critical frequency, and f is the observing frequency. As f decreases, h_c moves upward into regions of higher temperature T.

Kirchhoff's law, to which we called attention earlier in this chapter. A body can be a good radiator only if it is also a good absorber. Because of its transparency a piece of hot glass emits relatively little light, and by the same token the outer regions of the sun's atmosphere, which are transparent to radio waves of the frequency f, radiate only feebly at that frequency. The effective radiation level h_c is, then, simply the altitude at which the solar gas first becomes opaque enough to act as an effective radiator.

What is it that actually determines h_c? Clearly the answer must be related to the way in which the opacity of the solar gas varies with height. When radiation passes through a homogeneous absorbing medium, it is attenuated according to a law discovered by Bouguer in 1729:

$$I = I_0 e^{-\kappa s}, \qquad (4\text{-}7)$$

where I_0 is the initial intensity of the radiation and I is its intensity after it has traveled a distance s. The exponent κ is known as the *absorption coefficient* of the medium, since it obviously governs the rate at which attenuation occurs.* In a simple plasma like the solar gas, the absorption coefficient for a radio wave of frequency f is

$$\kappa \cong \frac{\gamma}{c} \left(\frac{f_0}{f}\right)^2, \qquad (4\text{-}8)$$

where γ is the average number of collisions that an electron in the gas experiences each second, c is the speed of light, and f_0 is the critical frequency for the plasma.

We can now see how κ might be expected to vary with altitude in the solar atmosphere. Equation (3-3) tells us that $f_0{}^2$ is proportional to the local electron density N, which of course increases as we move downward toward the denser regions of the atmosphere. Hence, if we start high in the corona and descend toward the photosphere, we encounter a constantly increasing critical frequency. It is evident from Eq. (4-8) that as long as f_0 is much less than the wave frequency f, the factor $(f_0/f)^2$ will keep the absorption small, but as f_0 approaches f, κ spurts upward and strong absorption sets in. Thus we see that the effective radiation level coincides with the altitude at which the critical frequency is approximately equal to the frequency of our radiation. Since f_0 increases *downward*, it is now obvious why the radiation level moves down as we make our observations at higher and higher frequencies.

We now understand why little energy of the frequency f is generated above h_c. Why is it that such energy cannot come from the levels *below* h_c? A simple argument can be based on the fact that the waves would have to escape through a region in which their frequency is less than the critical frequency. In the case of the earth's ionosphere we saw that this is impossible—the waves are reflected and turned back. A somewhat more rigorous way of looking at this involves the *index of refraction n* of the gas; just

---

* Often the product κs is replaced in Bouguer's law by the single symbol τ, which is called the *optical depth*. The reader can easily see from Eq. (4-7) that when the optical depth is unity (i.e., when $\tau = \kappa s = 1$), the radiation has been reduced to $1/e$ of its initial intensity.

as in optics, n is the ratio of the wavelength of the radiation in free space to that in the gas. For radio waves in a plasma

$$n = \sqrt{1 - (f_0/f)^2}. \qquad (4\text{-}9)$$

In the higher levels of the solar atmosphere, where f exceeds f_0, n is between one and zero. This means that propagation occurs in the usual manner, although its *phase* velocity exceeds c, the free-space velocity of light. But below h_c, where f is less than f_0, n turns into an imaginary number! Physically, this means that the waves simply cannot propagate under such conditions; the absorption coefficient κ has become effectively infinite. At the very lowest frequencies an additional complication is introduced by severe refraction, or bending of the ray paths, which has the effect of elevating the lower boundary of the radiation level. In Chapter 7 we shall have more to say about the role of refraction in the corona.

We have taken some pains to understand the existence of an effective radiation level because it is a general concept that has application far beyond the immediate problem of the apparent temperature of the solar atmosphere. In a wide variety of astrophysical sources this principle governs the emission, not only of radio waves but of optical radiation as well. We can now see, for example, that virtually all of the sun's light must come from the photosphere simply because that is the level at which the gases are opaque enough to visible wavelengths to radiate freely, and yet not so opaque as to prevent the emitted light from escaping.

The actual creation of thermal radio waves at the radiation level depends on a process known in quantum mechanics as a *free-free transition*. A free electron passing near a positive ion encounters a strong electrical attraction that accelerates it into a hyperbolic trajectory about the ion. The electron escapes and is once more "free," but during the brief instant of acceleration it emits a burst of radio energy as if to cry out in protest against being disturbed. Classical electromagnetic theory asserts that radiation must occur any time a charge is accelerated, and the resulting emission is often referred to by the German term *bremsstrahlung* or "braking radiation." If a hot plasma is sufficiently dense and opaque, the myriad free-free transitions that are constantly occurring establish a kind of thermal equilibrium, and the gas radiates like a blackbody of the same temperature.

THE DISTRIBUTION OF BRIGHTNESS

We have seen that the radiofrequency temperature of the sun depends strongly on the wavelength at which we make our observations. It may seem even stranger that the *size* of the radio sun should also vary with wavelength! However, a little thought will show that the two effects are related in a logical manner. The sun is hotter at long wavelengths because our radio telescope sees only the high-temperature outer corona. This being the case, it is only natural that the sun should also appear larger, since the diameter of the corona is of course much greater than that of the photosphere. After all, we are not surprised when eclipse photographs such as Plate VII show the combined corona and photosphere to be far more extensive than the photosphere alone.

Several kinds of instruments that were described in Chapter 3 have been used to measure the size and shape of the quiet sun. For mapping the solar disc at the very shortest wavelengths, it is difficult to improve on the single parabolic dish (Fig. 3-7). At longer wavelengths simple interferometers can provide one-dimensional scans, but a more useful instrument is a grating array, preferably in the form of a Christiansen cross whose pencil beams can trace out a detailed, two-dimensional solar map, as in Fig. 3-8. A major advantage of such mapping is that active regions can readily be identified and their effects subtracted from the desired picture of the quiet sun. Except at the time of sunspot minimum, it is no small problem merely to determine when the sun *is* completely quiet!

What do such studies show? Figure 4-7 is a composite diagram in which we can compare radio measurements made at six widely different wavelengths. Each curve represents the distribution of brightness temperature T_b along the solar equator. The figure illustrates in striking fashion the rapid growth of the radio sun in both size and temperature as the wavelength increases. At a wavelength of 3.7 m the solar disc is more than twice the diameter

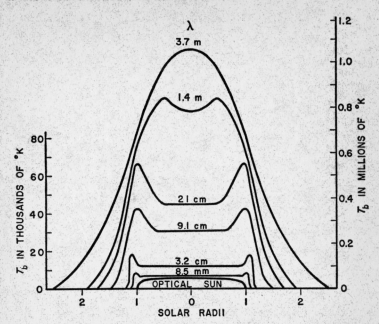

FIG. 4-7 Radiofrequency brightness distribution along the equator of the quiet sun at wavelengths ranging from 8.5 mm to 3.7 m. The upper two curves are to be read against the scale at the right, and the remaining curves against the scale at the left. For comparison with the radio data, the lowest curve shows the limb-darkened disc of the optical sun. (Data of various observers, after M. R. Kundu.[2])

of the photosphere. Also, a rather surprising phenomenon manifests itself in the so-called "bull's horn" shape of most of the curves. Over a wide range of wavelengths the radio sun shows marked limb *brightening,* in direct contrast to the limb *darkening* that occurs in the visible region of the spectrum.

How can we reconcile such contradictory behavior? If we remember the origin of the optical limb darkening, we need not search very far for an explanation. Because rays near the edge of the sun follow a longer atmospheric path and thus suffer more absorption (Fig. 2-3), the effective radiation level for such rays lies higher in the atmosphere in both the optical and the radio cases. Since the temperature of the photosphere *decreases* with altitude, this means that optical radiation near the limb comes from a cooler layer, resulting in limb darkening. But in the region of the solar atmosphere that is responsible for generating radio waves, the situation is completely reversed; the temperature *increases* with altitude, and thus the more elevated radiation layer near the limb appears brighter than the center of the disc.

Curiously enough, the radiofrequency limb brightening varies in marked fashion as we circle the rim of the sun. It is most conspicuous at the east and west limbs, but at the north and south poles the brightening is so reduced that it may even turn into limb *darkening* at some wavelengths. This effect is seen most easily in a two-dimensional map such as Fig. 4-8, where the

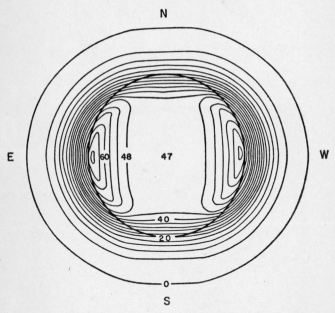

FIG. 4-8 A map of the quiet sun at a wavelength of 21 cm. The heavy circle outlines the visible disc. The contours represent the brightness temperature T_b at intervals of 4000° K, while the numbers give T_b in thousands of degrees. (After W. N. Christiansen and J. A. Warburton, from observations with a grating array.[3])

bright regions at the east and west limbs cause the diagram to resemble a head-on view of a giant housefly! It is obvious that in overall outline the radio sun is not circular, but elliptical in

Plate I. Historic 5-ft radio telescope with which Southworth and King first detected thermal waves from the sun. (Courtesy Dr. G. C. Southworth, with permission of Gordon and Breach.)

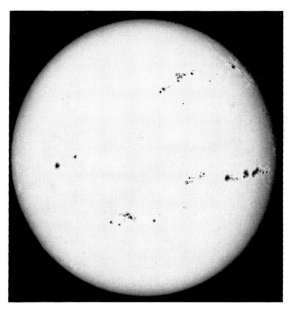

Plate II. The sun near sunspot maximum, December 21, 1957. (Courtesy Mount Wilson and Palomar Observatories.)

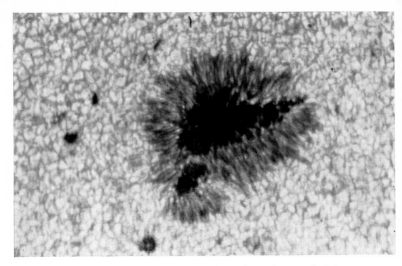

Plate III. A sunspot and the surrounding photosphere photographed from an unmanned Stratoscope balloon at an altitude of 80,000 ft. (Courtesy Dr. R. E. Danielson, Project Stratoscope, Princeton University.)

Plate IV. The new McMath solar telescope at Kitt Peak National Observatory in Arizona. (Courtesy Dr. A. K. Pierce.)

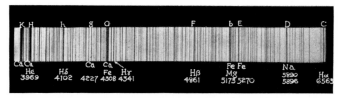

Plate V. The visible region of the solar spectrum. Numbers at the bottom are wavelengths in Angstroms of prominent absorption lines due to calcium, helium, hydrogen, iron, magnesium, and sodium. The letters at the top are historic designations given by Fraunhofer around 1817. (Yerkes Observatory, University of Chicago.)

Plate VI. A section of the solar limb showing the chromosphere with spicules thrusting upward into the lower corona. (Courtesy Sacramento Peak Observatory, Air Force Cambridge Research Laboratories.)

Plate VII. The corona during the solar eclipse of February 25, 1952. (Yerkes Observatory, University of Chicago.)

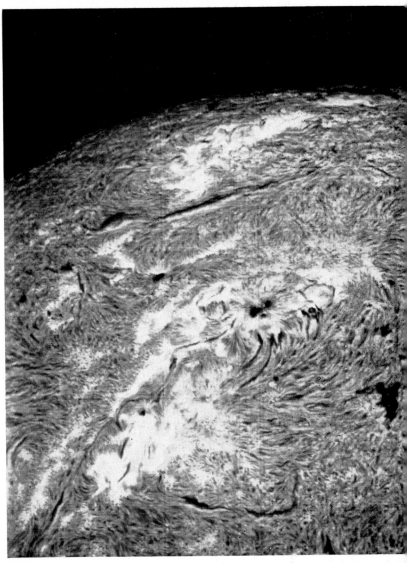

Plate VIII. Spectroheliogram of part of the sun's disc, made in the red light of the hydrogen-alpha line, May 4, 1958. (Courtesy Mount Wilson and Palomar Observatories.)

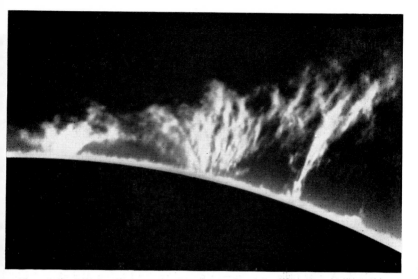

Plate IX. Prominences rising to a height of 80,000 miles above the chromosphere. Photographed in hydrogen light on August 21, 1909. (Courtesy Mount Wilson and Palomar Observatories.)

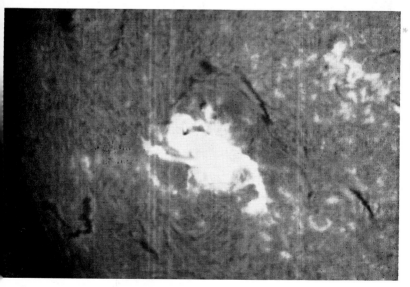

Plate X. Solar flare photographed in the light of the hydrogen-alpha line, July 16, 1959. (Courtesy Mount Wilson and Palomar Observatories.)

Plate XI. A solar radio telescope—the crossed grating interferometer of the Stanford University microwave spectroheliograph. (Courtesy Dr. R. N. Bracewell.)

Plate XII. Harvard University's solar radio observatory at Fort Davis, Texas. (Courtesy Dr. A. Maxwell.)

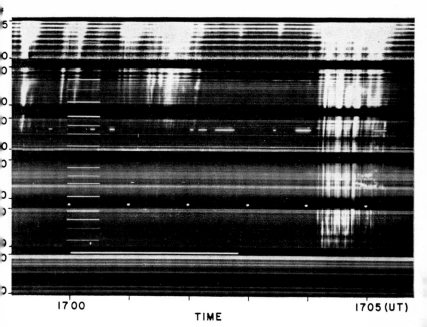

TIME

Plate XIII. Dynamic radio spectrogram showing groups of Type III fast drift bursts recorded during a 7-minute interval on April 1, 1960. The vertical scale shows the frequency f in Mc/sec, while the horizontal axis is a time scale marked in Universal Time, which is the same as Greenwich Mean Time. Note that the frequency scale is split into bands corresponding to the six individual receivers in the radio spectrograph. This spectrum and those in the plates that follow were recorded at Harvard's Fort Davis solar observatory; they are reproduced here through the kindness of the director, Dr. A. Maxwell.

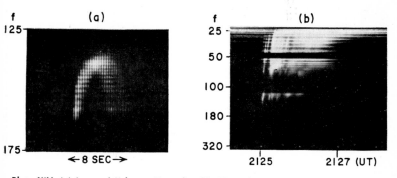

Plate XIV. (a) Inverted U burst, November 29, 1956. (b) Type V emission following several Type III bursts, February 1, 1960.

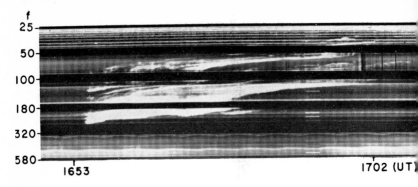

Plate XV. Type II burst with a strong second harmonic, April 9, 1959.

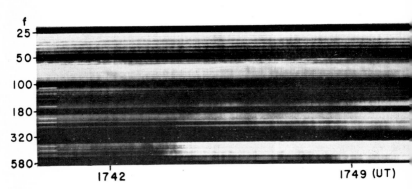

Plate XVI. Type IV emission, September 16, 1960.

form. Fortunately, this departure from circular symmetry is in good agreement with optical observations which show that there is a belt of unusually hot and dense coronal gas girdling the quiet sun above its equatorial regions.

Earlier in this chapter we saw that the radio emission from a blackbody might be expected to decrease as the inverse square of the wavelength [Eq. (4-2)]. Obviously the radio sun fails to behave like a simple blackbody, since both its size and its temperature change with wavelength. A little thought will show that each of these changes is in such a direction as to cause the flux to fall more slowly than $1/\lambda^2$. Over much of the observable radio spectrum the quiet-sun flux can be estimated roughly from the simple expression[4]

$$P_\lambda \cong \frac{1.5 \times 10^{-19}}{\lambda^{1.1}} \text{ w/m}^2/\text{cps,} \qquad (4\text{-}10)$$

where λ is in cm.

THE SUN AS A VARIABLE STAR

In the sprawling constellation of Cetus the Whale there is a star that bears the name *Mira,* which can be translated as "the wonderful." No doubt it was given this name because of its remarkable changes in brightness, which were discovered by Fabricius in 1596. Within a period of somewhat less than a year there is a thousand-fold variation in the light that we receive from Mira, although neither the period nor the amplitude of this fluctuation is entirely regular. Mira was the first recognized example of a *variable star,* but we now know that many of the stars behave in this fashion to a greater or lesser extent.

More than one line of evidence suggests that our own star, the sun, might be classified as a rather specialized kind of variable. For example, Fig. 4-5 indicates that over much of the radio spectrum the average brightness temperature of the quiet sun nearly doubles between sunspot minimum and sunspot maximum. Furthermore, these fluctuations in brightness are accompanied by changes in the *shape* of the radio sun, which is normally elliptical as we have seen in Fig. 4-8. During the increasing phase of the sunspot cycle the long axis of the ellipse (parallel to the sun's equator) expands by 15 or 20%, while there is little or no change in the short axis. As a consequence, the radio sun appears to be considerably more flattened near sunspot maximum.

Many scientists are convinced that large changes also occur in the ultraviolet radiation from the quiet sun. It has been suggested that in the extreme ultraviolet, at wavelengths below 1500 Å, the emission at sunspot maximum is double or even triple that at sunspot minimum. Because the earth's blanket of air prevents such short wavelengths from reaching instruments on the ground, our evidence thus far is largely indirect; the strongest clues have come from radio observations of the ionosphere, which is highly responsive to solar ultraviolet energy. Before long, observations from man-made satellites above the atmosphere will give us more direct information on the important question of solar variability. Such observations have already shown that the solar spectrum extends into the X-ray region, and that the average emission at these ultra-short wavelengths may vary as much as 50-fold over the solar cycle![5]

We have seen that the radiation from the quiet sun is subject to large variations at very long wavelengths and at very short wavelengths—that is, in the radio spectrum and in the ultraviolet and X-ray regions. How do these fluctuations affect the solar constant H, which is a measure of the total energy of all wavelengths that reaches the top of the earth's atmosphere? Is H actually a "constant," or is the term a misnomer? While this question has been hotly debated for many decades, recent studies suggest that any *real* variations in the accepted value of 2.00 cal/cm^2/min must be smaller than 0.3%, a limit set by the accuracy of the observations themselves. (Of course, the earth follows an elliptical orbit about the sun, and the changing earth-sun distance causes an *apparent* annual variation in H of ±3.4%.)

How can we reconcile the near-constancy of H with the marked changes in energy that seem to occur at the two extremes of the spectrum? The answer is that these antipodes contribute only a tiny fraction of the total energy that makes up the overall solar constant, and thus their fluctuations cannot affect the value of H in any important way. Figure 4-9 is a sketch of the approximate

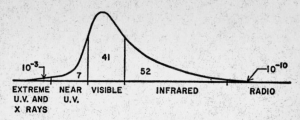

FIG. 4-9 Schematic diagram of the distribution of energy in the solar spectrum (not to scale). The numbers are percentages of the solar constant, $H = 2.00$ cal/cm^2/min $= 1390$ w/m^2. The figure for the radio energy is for the observed band from 15 to 30,000 Mc/sec.

distribution of energy in the various divisions of the sun's spectrum. We see that the extreme ultraviolet and X-ray regions contribute only 0.001% of the solar constant, while the observable radio spectrum is still more parsimonious. Little wonder, then, that even major changes in these regions are incapable of producing observable fluctuations in H.

While it may be scientifically unexciting, the stability of the solar constant should be a cause for rejoicing, rather than disappointment. Any marked variation in H would almost certainly alter the climate of the world in which we live. Like genetic mutations, the majority of such changes would be undesirable, to say nothing of being unpredictable. Some geophysicists have even speculated that a modest *increase* in H might perversely bring on a new ice age because of increased precipitation. The unsolved riddle of past ice ages hints darkly that the solar furnace may not always have been as dependable as we have found it to be during the brief span of recorded history.

REFERENCES

1. Allen, C. W., "The Variation of Decimetre-Wave Radiation with Solar Activity," Monthly Not. Roy. Astron. Soc. London **117**, 174-188 (1957).

2. Kundu, M. R., *Solar Radio Astronomy* (John Wiley & Sons, Inc., New York, 1965), pp. 134-135.

3. Christiansen, W. N. and Warburton, J. A., "The Sun in Two Dimensions at 21 Cm," Observatory **75**, 9-13 (1955).

4. Rush, J. H. and Evans, J. W., "The Sun," in *Handbook of Geophysics* (The Macmillan Co., New York, 1960), p. 17-7.
5. National Academy of Sciences, "Current Status of the Solar Cycle and Summary of Solar-Geophysical Activity," Trans. Am. Geophys. Union **46**, 484-487 (1965).

FOR FURTHER READING

Jager, C. de, "Structure and Dynamics of the Solar Atmosphere," in *Handbuch der Physik*, Vol. 52, edited by S. Flugge (Springer-Verlag, Berlin, 1959), pp. 286-296.

Wild, J. P., "The Radio Emission of the Sun," in *Radio Astronomy Today*, edited by H. P. Palmer, R. D. Davies, and M. I. Large (Manchester University Press, Manchester, 1963).

Solar System Radio Astronomy, edited by J. Aarons (Plenum Press, Inc., New York, 1965), Chapters 3-6.

5 Radio Signals from the Active Sun

A scientist derives an excitement from his work that is very much like the pleasure other people take in solving puzzles. In either case, the more challenging the problem, the greater the satisfaction that comes from a proper solution. However, in the radio spectrum of the active sun the scientific problem solver has been confronted with an embarrassment of riches, for the phenomena are almost bewildering in their complexity and variability.

Over a period of time radio astronomers have learned how to classify the more important kinds of events into half-a-dozen categories, and to relate these categories to each other and to solar phenomena in general. The process has been not unlike the biological problem of grouping widely different species of animals into the proper genus, family, order, class, and phylum. Out of such grouping, the beginnings of real understanding are emerging. In the following pages we shall look briefly at a number of solar radio phenomena and attempt to relate them to the physics of the sun in terms of present-day ideas. Like Alice stepping through the looking glass, we shall encounter a number of concepts that may seem strange to many readers although they are at the forefront of modern thought in physics and astronomy —concepts such as cyclotron and synchrotron emission, Cerenkov radiation, plasma waves, and leaky magnetic bottles.

THE SLOWLY VARYING COMPONENT

If we have the patience to make daily measurements of solar radio flux over long periods of time, we find that the day-to-day variations are extremely small so long as our operating wavelength is less than 1 cm. But beginning at wavelengths just above this, we notice that erratic increases in the general flux level are often superimposed on the steady background of thermal radiation. These changes amount to a few percent of the original quiet-sun level, and they last for periods measured in days or weeks. Because of this protracted time scale, the radio flux that causes the increases is referred to as the *slowly varying component*, a rather cumbersome term often abbreviated to *S-component*.

In Fig. 5-1 we see that as the wavelength increases above 1 cm the S-component at first grows in intensity. Since the normal thermal flux of the quiet sun declines with increasing wavelength, the fluctuations soon become relatively more important. In the "decimeter" region between 10 and 50 cm the slowly varying component is quite conspicuous, but then it disappears in the meter wavelength range, to be replaced by an entirely different set of phenomena that we shall discuss later.

An early clue to the origin of the slowly varying component came from studies which showed that its intensity rose and fell in near-synchronism with the sunspot number R. If the comparison is made with the total *area* of the spots on the visible face of the sun, the correlation is even more striking. The results of such a study, made during a one-year period, are shown in Fig. 5-2. It would be difficult to deny that here we have strong circumstantial evidence linking the S-component to sunspots!

Should we accept the simple conclusion that the spots themselves are directly responsible for the radiation? Apparently not, for in most cases the enhanced emission far outlives individual sunspots. In Fig. 5-2 we see that the slowly varying component shows a strong tendency to recur at intervals of about 27 days, corresponding to the average rotational period of the most active zones of the sun. Apparently the sources of the emission often

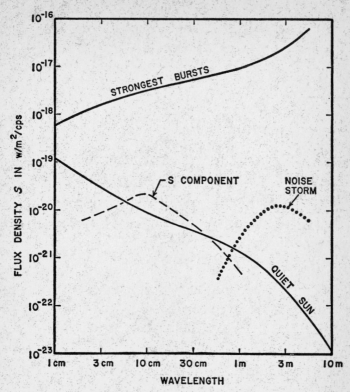

FIG. 5-1 Received radio flux density due to various components of the radiation from the active sun. The spectrum of the quiet sun is shown for comparison. Values for the slowly varying component apply to levels reached near sunspot maximum. (Data for the quiet sun and for noise storms from C. W. Allen;[1] for bursts from J. P. Wild, S. F. Smerd, and A. A. Weiss;[2] and for the S-component from M. R. Kundu.[3])

survive several complete solar rotations, implying a life span that would be remarkable for a sunspot.

As long ago as 1946 direct observations began to link the S-component with chromospheric plages, which, as we saw in Chapter 2, form over active regions and often last for months. The first evidence came from studies of solar eclipses, about which we shall have more to say in the next chapter. Later,

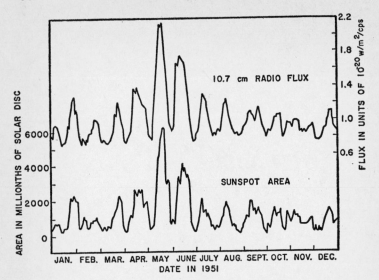

FIG. 5-2 Correlation between sunspot areas and the slowly varying component of the solar radio flux during 1951. (After A. E. Covington and W. J. Medd.[4])

W. N. Christiansen and his colleagues in Australia began a brilliant series of developments in high-resolution radio telescopes that ultimately settled the matter. Christiansen's first major instrument was a grating interferometer formed by 32 parabolic dishes spaced along a 700-ft baseline.[5] At its operating wavelength of 21 cm the array created a pattern of fan beams 3' of arc wide, through which the sun drifted each day to produce a number of one-dimensional scans of the solar disc. (The reader should keep in mind the fact that the apparent diameter of the sun itself is about 32' of arc.) Figure 5-3 shows a sequence of such scans, spaced at intervals of two days. In this series we see a strong radio source appearing at the east limb and being carried across the disc by the sun's rotation.

Christiansen's second innovation was the crossed interferometer that has since been given his name (see Chapter 3). In the original Christiansen cross, 64 parabolic dishes were arrayed in two arms 1200 ft long. Operating at a wavelength of 21 cm, the instrument produced a series of narrow pencil beams with which

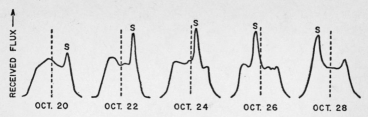

FIG. 5-3 A radio plage S rotating across the face of the sun during October, 1952. In each case the east limb of the sun is to the right, while a dashed line marks the center of the disc. (After W. N. Christiansen and J. A. Warburton.[5])

the Australians were able to scan the sun in two dimensions, at last making it possible to synthesize a complete radio map of the solar disc. For an example of such a map, the reader is referred to Fig. 3-8, which was produced by a later American version of the Christiansen cross.

When such maps are compared with photographs taken in monochromatic light (Plate VIII), the regions of intense radio emission are found in nearly every case to coincide with the familiar optical plages. Thus the sources of the S-component have come to be called *radio plages*. Although the diameters of these features normally range from 3' to 8' of arc, M. R. Kundu has shown that radio plages which overlie active sunspots often have much smaller, intense "nuclei" that correspond in size and location with the spots themselves.

At what level in the solar atmosphere do we find radio plages? By borrowing a page from Galileo's notebook, we can determine the altitude of such a feature merely by measuring the speed with which it appears to cross the visible disc. As seen from the earth, a marking on the photosphere will of course take about half a solar rotation (perhaps 13 or 14 days) to transit the face of the sun from one limb to the other. On the other hand, as we see in Fig. 5-4, a source S high above the photosphere will seem to move across the solar disc far more swiftly, completing its passage when the sun has turned through an angle ϵ that is considerably less than 180°. When the object is seen near the middle of the disc, its apparent linear speed is proportional to its actual distance from the center of the sun, from which the

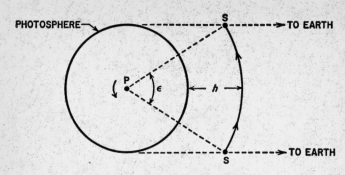

FIG. 5-4 Passage of an elevated source S across the face of the sun. P is the sun's north pole, while the earth is to be visualized as situated far to the right.

altitude h can be determined. In this way it has been found that radio plages lie at levels from 10,000 to 100,000 km above the photosphere and, as in the case of the quiet sun, the longest wavelengths originate at the greatest altitudes. It is interesting to note that this method of measuring solar altitudes was used by Galileo to quiet several rivals who insisted that sunspots were in reality dark satellites of the sun which were occasionally seen against the brilliant disc.

What is the physical nature of a radio plage? A combined attack by radio and optical methods has given us a picture of such a disturbance as a dome of gas rising as high as 100,000 km above an active region. Because the density within the dome is 5 or 10 times that of the surrounding atmosphere, optical astronomers refer to these features as *coronal condensations*. At higher altitudes they probably merge into the beautiful *coronal streamers* that often appear in eclipse photographs such as Plate VII. While the temperature measurements are rather discordant, they suggest that the gas in a radio plage is not extraordinarily hot compared with the surrounding corona. Apparently the enhanced emission results more from the high density of the dome than from its temperature.

Astronomers have generally assumed that the S-component is simple thermal radiation, generated as in the case of the quiet sun by free-free transitions of electrons. However, we have seen that well-behaved thermal flux should decrease steadily as the wavelength increases, whereas the S-component shows a distinct maximum at a wavelength of about 10 cm (Fig. 5-1). According to Russian and Japanese theoreticians, this embarrassing peak may indicate that a portion of the slowly varying component is actually *gyromagnetic emission* from electrons accelerated in the strong magnetic fields that permeate active regions.

Just what do we mean by "gyromagnetic emission"? Since it is the first of several kinds of *nonthermal* emission with which we shall be concerned, it will pay us to digress for a moment in order to understand it better. In general, thermal radiation results from *random* motions of particles, whereas nonthermal emission occurs because some agency, such as a magnetic field, has introduced *order* into the motions of the electrons. Every student of physics knows that an electron which is injected into a magnetic field at some arbitrary angle is forced to spiral around the field lines. The *gyrofrequency* f_H with which the electron circles the lines is given by

$$f_H = \frac{Be}{2\pi mc} \text{ cycles/sec,} \tag{5-1}$$

where B is the magnetic field in gauss, e is the charge of the electron in electrostatic units, m is the mass of the electron, and c is the speed of light. By combining the constants we obtain the simple equation:

$$f_H = 2.8B \text{ Mc/sec.} \tag{5-2}$$

Since the spiraling electron is constantly being accelerated, it is obliged to radiate, and it normally does so at the gyrofrequency. The resulting electromagnetic energy is often called *cyclotron radiation*, because the whirling charges in a laboratory cyclotron emit in this manner. In the solar atmosphere the frequency f_H always encounters a region in which the absorption coefficient κ is infinite, and thus it is unable to escape. However, if the initial energy of the electron is in the so-called *relativistic* range,* where its speed is an appreciable fraction of c, it will

---

* By "relativistic" we imply that the velocity v of a particle is high enough so that its apparent mass m has increased noticeably according to the relationship $m = m_0/\sqrt{1 - (v/c)^2}$. Here m_0 is the ordinary *rest mass* of the particle. For a discussion of relativity, see Momentum No. 9, *An Introduction to the Special Theory of Relativity*, by R. Katz.

radiate not only the fundamental gyrofrequency, but a number of harmonics of f_H as well. Since they occur at higher frequencies, the harmonics may be able to escape through the solar atmosphere without serious absorption, and it is these harmonics that are credited with creating the nonthermal peak in the S-component spectrum. From the details of this spectrum it is inferred that the magnetic fields in the radio plages must range from 250 to 600 gauss.

Radio observations of the slowly varying component have given us new insight into the critical layers of the sun's atmosphere just above the active regions. Special interest is attached to these plage areas since rocket-borne cameras have shown that they are the seat of continuous X-ray emission which exerts a powerful influence on the terrestrial ionosphere that stretches over our heads. Moreover, these regions spawn the solar flares whose spectacular outbursts of radio energy will be described in the following sections.

RADIO EVENTS OF A SMALL FLARE

Astronomers indicate the relative size and brightness of a flare by assigning to it an *importance number* ranging from 1 to 3, with plus and minus signs being used to add nuances to the scale. Events rated as 1 or 1— occur with great frequency when the sun is active, but they are of such small magnitude that many must escape detection. On the other hand, a 3+ flare is an eruption of such enormous magnitude that only a few outbursts of this size occur during a sunspot cycle. All flares are accompanied by enhanced radio emission, but the intensity and complexity of the radiation generally increase with the importance number. In this section we shall consider the more limited range of radio phenomena that is typical of modest flares with low importance numbers.

The Gradual Rise and Fall. The first warning that flare activity may be on its way is often provided by a slow increase in the microwave emission from a small region of a radio plage. In many cases the event never reaches an explosive phase, and the radio flux unobtrusively sinks back to its original level, fol-

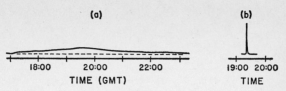

FIG. 5-5 Microwave bursts recorded at 10.7 cm wavelength: (a) Gradual rise and fall, April 14, 1957; (b) an impulsive burst, December 15, 1948. (After A. E. Covington.[6])

lowing a pattern like that of Fig. 5-5(a). Known by the somewhat unimaginative title of *gradual rise and fall,* the phenomenon is believed to result from the rapid contraction of a local magnetic field. The contraction squeezes the plasma contained in the field, and as usual the act of compression heats the enclosed gas. According to this picture, the gradual rise and fall is merely thermal radiation from free-free transitions of electrons in a temporary "magnetic furnace."

Impulsive Bursts. On some occasions the underlying mechanism that produces the gradual rise and fall suddenly becomes wildly unstable, and the explosive events that characterize a solar flare ensue. We are largely concerned with the phenomena that take place during the early stages or "flash phase" of the eruption. Within as little as 1 minute the microwave brightness temperature of a small area of the plage may increase a hundredfold to 10^8 ° K, marking the beginning of a so-called *impulsive burst.* Figure 5-5(b) shows a typical example of this type of microwave burst.

Strangely enough, the radio event is often accompanied by a remarkably similar burst of penetrating X-rays, which can be detected in space beyond the earth's atmosphere by instruments mounted in rockets or artificial satellites. It is believed that the X-rays are bremsstrahlung created by free-free transitions of high-speed electrons ejected from the flare, the same radiation mechanism that is responsible for the thermal radio energy of the quiet sun. However, the spectrum of the microwave burst itself is not that of ordinary thermal emission, for it shows a broad maximum at wavelengths near 10 cm.

What, then, *is* the process by which an impulsive burst is

emitted? It has been suggested that the mechanism is that of *synchrotron radiation,* a name derived from a special type of high-energy laboratory cyclotron in which such emission was initially discovered in 1947. The synchrotron process is of the greatest importance, for astronomers now credit it with much of the energy that comes to us from a wide variety of celestial sources. Let us therefore digress again to examine it in more detail.

Earlier in the chapter we found that when an electron enters a magnetic field with a speed in the relativistic range it emits a number of harmonics of the gyrofrequency f_H, as well as the fundamental gyrofrequency itself. Now, the more nearly the electron speed approaches the speed of light, the more numerous and prominent the harmonics become, until the fundamental frequency virtually disappears and all of the radiation is finally concentrated in a very large number of harmonics which are so closely spaced that they merge together to form a broad continuum. At this point, the transition from ordinary cyclotron emission to synchrotron radiation is complete.

Figure 5-6 shows a typical synchrotron spectrum, which is best

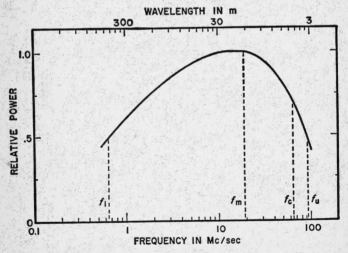

FIG. 5-6 Spectrum of synchrotron radiation from an electron of 20 Mev energy in a magnetic field of 0.01 gauss.

described in terms of a *characteristic frequency* f_c. If E is the energy of the electron in millions of electron volts* (Mev), and B is the magnetic field strength in gauss, then

$$f_c = 16\ BE^2 \quad \text{Mc/sec.} \tag{5-3}$$

The spectrum displays a broad peak at a frequency $f_m \cong 0.3f_c$, while the radiation falls to half of its peak value at the frequencies $f_l \cong 0.011f_c$ and $f_u \cong 1.47f_c$. Of course, if the emission comes from a great many electrons of different energies the spectrum will be smeared out over a still wider range of frequencies.

A curious property of synchrotron radiation is that nearly all of the energy is beamed into a narrow cone that opens in the direction toward which the electron is traveling. Thus, if the electron is being whirled in a circle, as in Fig. 5-7, the emission

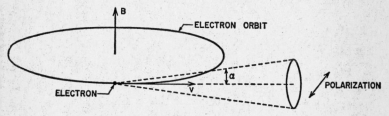

FIG. 5-7 Emission cone for synchrotron radiation from an electron of mass m and energy E; v is the instantaneous velocity of the electron. The half-angle of the cone, α, is equal to mc^2/E rad.

is largely confined to a flat disc perpendicular to the magnetic field. An observer in the plane of the disc receives a brief pulse of radiation each time the electron passes a certain point in its orbit—indeed, the form of the synchrotron spectrum can be attributed to the fact that a sharp pulse cannot be represented by a single frequency, but must be synthesized from a multitude of harmonics according to principles set forth in the mathematical field of *Fourier analysis*. In a general way we can now understand the form of Eq. (5-3); as the electron energy E increases

* An electron volt is the energy acquired by an electron that has been accelerated through a potential difference of one volt; it is equal to 1.6×10^{-12} erg.

the radiation cone narrows and the observed pulse becomes still sharper, requiring an even greater spread in the frequencies that represent it. From the observer's position near the plane of the orbit, the electron appears to oscillate back and forth with a linear motion, and thus the synchrotron emission is received as a linearly polarized wave with the plane of polarization perpendicular to the magnetic field B.

Because the synchrotron process requires a magnetic field, it seems especially likely to occur in the strong fields associated with solar active regions. According to the Japanese astronomer T. Takakura, the shape, intensity, spectrum, and polarization of the impulsive bursts are all consistent with synchrotron radiation from electrons of relativistic energy orbiting in a magnetic field of about 1000 gauss. Presumably these are the same electrons that generate the accompanying bursts of X-rays.

Type III Bursts. We have seen that the onset of a flare is often accompanied by two kinds of microwave emission—the gradual rise and fall and the impulsive bursts. However, the radio signals that are the most spectacular and most characteristic of the flash phase of a flare occur at wavelengths in the meter range. These are the *Type III bursts,* which are also known by the more descriptive term "fast drift bursts." (Since we shall soon encounter several types of bursts distinguished by Roman numerals, readers who are inclined to worry about such things are warned that the numbers have no physical significance, but are merely arbitrary labels that have become fixed through usage. Thus it is not especially illogical that we should meet Type III before Types I and II!)

On many days Type III bursts completely dominate solar records made at meter wavelengths. While individual bursts last no more than a few seconds, they tend to occur in groups that may continue for several minutes, as we see in Plate XIII. By far the most striking characteristic of Type III emission is a rapid drift of each burst from high to low frequencies during its brief life span. It was this behavior that gave rise to the name "fast drift bursts," and it causes the bursts to appear as steeply sloping lines on swept-frequency records such as Plate XIII. Often a burst is accompanied by a second harmonic—that is, by a companion burst at twice the frequency of the original. Type III emission is observed over the wavelength range from about 0.5 m (600 Mc/sec) to the longest wavelengths that penetrate the terrestrial ionosphere. At times the waves are unpolarized, but on other occasions they display circular or elliptical polarization.

What could cause the rapid frequency drift that gives a Type III burst such a distinctive character? In Chapter 4 we saw that the radiation from the quiet sun decreases in frequency as we go higher in the solar atmosphere. Back in 1950 the Australian J. P. Wild suggested that fast drift bursts might arise from disturbances speeding outward through the corona and, by analogy, radiating lower and lower frequencies as their altitude increases. Since a crude value for the rate-of-change of frequency with height had already been established for the corona, Wild was able to estimate how fast the disturbances would have to rise in order to produce the observed drift rates of from 10 to 100 Mc/sec per second. The required velocities turned out to be as great as one-third of the speed of light, which at the time seemed rather implausible.

Nevertheless, with the kind of tenacity that characterizes good science, Wild and his associates erected a special swept-frequency interferometer to put the hypothesis of the moving sources to an experimental test.[7] The instrument scanned the frequency band from 40 to 70 Mc/sec twice each second, and by virtue of its 1-km baseline it was able to pinpoint the locations of radio sources with an accuracy of 1' of arc. Figure 5-8 shows data derived from several of the many burst records obtained with the new interferometer. It is evident that the source position does indeed change with frequency in a systematic way, with the lowest frequencies coming from the greatest altitudes. Since the frequency invariably progresses from high to low during a burst, there was no longer any reason to doubt that the sources were indeed racing away from the solar surface at speeds which ranged from $0.2c$ to $0.8c$! (Occasionally a source seems to reach a maximum height and then plummet back toward the sun, producing an "inverted U burst" such as we see in Plate XIV.)

What is the nature of these speeding sources? Because their radio brightness temperatures range up to 10^{11} ° K, a simple

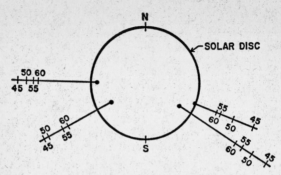

FIG. 5-8 Source position as a function of frequency for Type III bursts arising from four flares near the solar limb. The numbers along the burst trajectories are frequencies in Mc/sec, showing the position at which each frequency was observed to arise; the optical positions of the flares are indicated by black dots. (After J. P. Wild, K. V. Sheridan, and A. A. Neylan.[7])

thermal origin is out of the question. Wild and his colleagues believe that the emission arises from *Cerenkov plasma waves* that are excited by streams of fast electrons shot out from the parent flares.[2] The name "Cerenkov" is borrowed from a peculiar kind of optical emission that occurs when atomic particles race through a transparent medium at speeds exceeding the phase velocity of light in that medium.* For example, the eerie blue light seen in the liquid shield surrounding certain types of nuclear reactors is Cerenkov radiation.

Since the entire subject of plasma waves is one of many complexities, some of which are not yet resolved, we can treat it here only in a somewhat superficial manner. A plasma is of course nothing more than an ionized gas, in which there is normally a uniform distribution of positive and negative charges—that is, of heavy positive ions and the far lighter and more mobile electrons.† In a sense, such a medium displays elastic properties analogous to those which permit ordinary substances to transmit sound waves. If a passing disturbance creates a local excess in the electron population, electrical forces are set up which repel electrons away from this region. However, like a swing that has

* See Momentum No. 7, *Polarized Light*, by W. A. Shurcliff and S. S. Ballard.

† See Momentum No. 11, *Plasmas—Laboratory and Cosmic*, by F. Boley.

been set in motion, the retreating electrons overshoot their equilibrium positions and continue to oscillate back and forth at the so-called *plasma frequency,* which proves to be nothing more than our old friend f_0, the critical frequency of the medium [see Eqs. (3-3) and (3-4)]. Such oscillations propagate through the plasma as longitudinal waves* consisting of alternating condensations and rarefactions in the electron population, very much like sound waves in an ordinary gas.

Now, the speed of a plasma wave in the corona is less than that of light, and the wave can thus be outraced by the very electrons that generate it—a situation somewhat analogous to the jet aircraft whose speed is greater than that of the noise it makes. It is this circumstance that is characteristic of a Cerenkov process. Under these conditions the wave continues to grow in intensity by absorbing energy from the passing electron stream, a form of amplification referred to by plasma physicists as *two-stream instability.* Does the amplified plasma wave immediately give rise to electromagnetic radiation of frequency f_0—that is, to radio waves? Apparently not, for the plasma wave is longitudinal, while electromagnetic waves are transverse, and the one is not likely to excite the other unless some "coupling" mechanism is present to aid in the conversion process.

In the solar corona the necessary coupling can be provided either by *inhomogeneities* or by *scattering.* The inhomogeneities may take the form of relatively large-scale variations in the plasma density or in the local magnetic field. This method of converting a plasma wave into an electromagnetic wave is most effective if the plasma wave is traveling downward along magnetic field lines toward the denser regions of the lower corona. The resulting radio wave is also directed downward toward the photosphere, and we can thus receive it only by reflection. Because of these directional characteristics, wave coupling through inhomogeneities does not seem to be very appropriate for the generation of Type III emission; however, as we shall see later, it may play an important role in other kinds of bursts.

* In a *longitudinal* wave the oscillatory motion is parallel to the direction in which the wave is traveling, while in a *transverse* wave the oscillations are perpendicular to this direction.

Conversion through scattering occurs when the plasma wave encounters numerous small-scale irregularities in the background plasma density. Such irregularities are nothing more than momentary clumps of particles produced by the random thermal motions of the ions and electrons. If the scattering is caused by an ion clump, a radio wave is generated that has the same frequency f_0 and direction of motion as the incident plasma wave. On the other hand, if the scattering is due to an electron clump the resulting electromagnetic wave has a frequency $2f_0$, *double* that of the original plasma wave. The Russian theoreticians V. L. Ginzburg and V. V. Zhelezniakov have pointed to the existence of a second harmonic in Type III bursts as a natural consequence of the scattering of plasma waves by *both* ion and electron clumps, and thus the scattering mechanism appears to be well adapted to explaining these bursts. The conversion of plasma energy into electromagnetic waves is a grossly wasteful process. While the scattering mechanism is perhaps 30 times more efficient than the rival process of coupling through large-scale inhomogeneities, at best only about 3 parts per million of the energy in the plasma wave finally appears as radio energy!

According to the above interpretation, then, we picture Type III bursts as being generated by swift streams of electrons soaring upward through the corona. At each level the electrons excite plasma waves, which oscillate at the local critical frequency, f_0. Finally, the plasma waves are converted into the observed radio waves of frequencies f_0 and $2f_0$, probably by scattering from small clumps of positive ions and electrons.

Interpreted in this way, studies of Type III bursts can provide us with additional information about the critical frequencies at various levels in the solar atmosphere. Through Eq. (3-4) these frequencies can be translated into electron densities, thereby contributing to our knowledge of the physical structure of the corona. Interestingly enough, as we see in Fig. 5-9, the densities along the burst trajectories seem to be considerably higher than is normal in the surrounding corona. When electron clouds are ejected from flares, they apparently prefer to race outward along coronal streamers, which are columns of unusually high density in the sun's atmosphere.

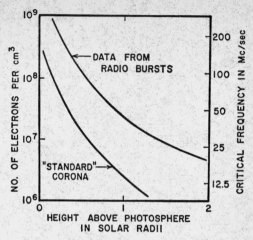

FIG. 5-9 Electron densities and critical frequencies at various altitudes in the solar atmosphere. The lower curve represents the so-called Baumbach-Allen standard corona. (After A. A. Weiss.[8])

Type V Bursts. Roughly 10% of the Type III burst groups are followed by a short period of continuous emission, which has been referred to as "afterglow." Less poetically, such an event is classified as a *Type V burst.* The radiation ordinarily lasts from 1 to 5 minutes, and on a swept-frequency spectrogram it appears as an amorphous blob extending over a wide range of frequencies below 200 Mc/sec (see Plate XIV).

The spectrum, duration, and intensity of Type V emission led Wild to suggest that it is synchrotron radiation from the same speeding electron streams that excite the associated Type III bursts. Since the Type V sources seemed to show little or no movement, Wild supposed that the electrons had finally become "trapped" in tangled magnetic fields far out in the corona. Such trapping would halt the motion of the electron cloud as a whole, but inside the cloud individual electrons would continue to dash back and forth at high speed, imitating the trapped particles in the earth's Van Allen belts. Unfortunately, recent observations have created serious objections to this model, and at present the origin of Type V bursts (like a multitude of other solar problems!) is open to question.

Summary. In a discussion such as this, where we have had to digress into a number of details, it is easy to lose sight of the overall phenomenon. With the aid of Fig. 5-10, let us

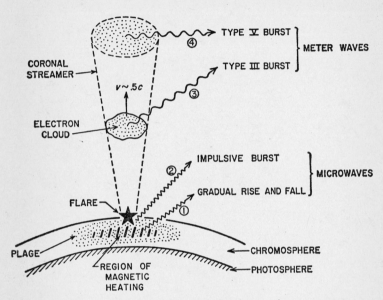

FIG. 5-10 Highly schematic representation of typical radio phenomena accompanying a small flare. Numbers in circles indicate the usual sequence of events. The "puff" in which the electron cloud is born is sometimes visible to optical astronomers.

quickly recapitulate the typical radio events associated with a small flare. First, local magnetic heating in a chromospheric plage results in microwave activity known as the gradual rise and fall, suggesting that a flare may be imminent. If the flare actually materializes, one or more swarms of relativistic electrons are ejected outward through the corona, exciting plasma oscillations which appear at meter wavelengths as the brief but spectacular Type III fast drift bursts. Other electrons are driven downward into the denser chromosphere, where they emit microwave impulsive bursts by the synchrotron process, as well as bursts of X-rays. Finally, the debris of the flare may somehow generate several minutes of continuous, low-frequency radiation identified as a Type V burst. The picture presented here owes a great deal to Wild and his co-workers. Although it is not universally accepted, it is nevertheless a useful and generally convincing model of a complex physical process.

THE AFTERMATH OF A LARGE FLARE

The events we have just described are typical of the flash phase of a small flare. Indeed, unless its importance number is 2 or more, it is unlikely that the flare will ever develop beyond this stage, which we have found to be characterized by the ejection of a cloud of fast electrons. Even if the flare is a large one, it passes through a similar flash phase, but it may in addition disgorge a cloud of plasma. The eruption of this mass of matter gives rise to a whole new set of radio phenomena that follow on the heels of the events of the flash phase. Figure 5-11 is an

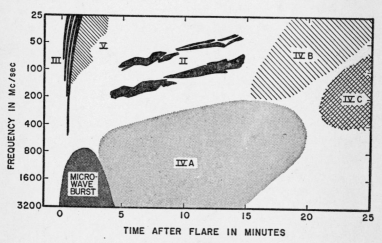

FIG. 5-11 An idealized sketch of the radio phenomena accompanying a large flare, as they might be displayed by a wide-band radio spectrograph. The Roman numerals indicate the major types of emission.

attempt to display, in idealized form, a sequence of events that might be typical of a large flare. Since no two such sequences are ever quite alike, the reader should understand that here we must use the word "typical" as we would in speaking of a "typical thunderstorm." Individual specimens may vary enormously in size, in form, and in behavior!

Type II Bursts. The flare's opening moments are punctuated by Type III bursts and perhaps by Type V emission. Several minutes after the fast drift bursts have died away, a new kind of burst appears. Designated as *Type II,* these bursts resemble their predecessors in several important respects, displaying both a second harmonic and a systematic drift in frequency. However, their frequency drift is much slower than that of a Type III event, seldom exceeding 1 Mc/sec per second, and they ordinarily last for 10 minutes or so, rather than for just a few seconds. Not unexpectedly, they are often called "slow drift bursts." The second harmonic appears more than half of the time in Type II emission, whereas it is much rarer in fast drift bursts. A well-defined Type II burst with a strong second harmonic is shown in Plate XV.

The qualitative resemblance of Types II and III naturally suggests that we are dealing with related phenomena. It is generally agreed that the slow drift bursts also arise in plasma oscillations excited by some outward-moving disturbance, but the frequency drift corresponds to a speed of "only" 1000 km/sec. Since this speed is nevertheless 10 times that of sound in the corona, it is believed that the disturbance may be a supersonic *shock wave* created by the explosive eruption of matter that accompanies the flash phase of the flare. High-resolution observations show that a single Type II burst may come from several rather widely separated sources, suggesting that the explosion has produced a fragmented shock wave with several components shooting off in different directions.[8]

A curious feature of certain Type II events is that they show a fine structure, almost as if they were actually made up of a large number of closely spaced Type III bursts. It is possible that the moving shock front accelerates the electrons of the solar atmosphere to high speeds, and these electrons then generate fast drift bursts in the manner described earlier. There is now evidence from space probes that such electron acceleration occurs at the shock front where the solar wind impinges on the earth's magnetic field (see Fig. 8-5). Some astronomers believe that all Type II events are simply superpositions of myriads of Type III bursts created in this manner.

Even near sunspot maximum, Type II bursts occur, on the average, only about once every 50 hours. This can be contrasted with an average rate of occurrence of Type III bursts of one every few minutes! These figures are of course related to the relative frequency of large and small flares. Only 2% of the flares of importance 1 produce Type II bursts, whereas 30% of the flares of importance 3 generate such emission.

Type IV Bursts. Since the earliest systematic observations of the radio sun, it has been known that great outbursts of radio noise are sometimes followed by long periods of continuous emission that is remarkable for its steadiness and lack of burst structure. When radio spectrographs became available, they showed that this radiation often covered the entire spectrum, from the longest to the shortest wavelengths (see Plate XVI). Such long-enduring, continuous emission following a flare is now classified as a *Type IV burst,* although the term "burst" may seem rather inappropriate for an event that can last for hours. In a limited sense, one might think of Type IV radiation as a period of continuous emission following a slow drift burst, just as the Type V continuum was found to follow fast drift bursts. This analogy is useful for mnemonic purposes, but it should not be pressed too far.

The relative steadiness of Type IV emission is in a way deceptive, for it now appears that at least three different kinds of sources may be involved. Furthermore, Type IV bursts vary so extensively among themselves that it is even harder to describe a "typical" event than was the case for other solar bursts. Because of this complexity a number of different models and systems of nomenclature have been used, and even today radio astronomers find it difficult to agree on the details of Type IV radiation.

At least one variety of Type IV emission can "jump the gun" and precede the accompanying Type II burst. As we see in Fig. 5-11, such radiation begins during the flash phase, but is confined to the microwave region of the spectrum. Following Kundu, we shall refer to it as *Type IVA.* The source of the emission is a small region, 4' of arc or less in diameter, that remains motionless near the parent flare. Since we find a wide band of frequencies coming from the same small volume of the solar atmosphere, it is generally assumed that the synchrotron process is involved, and the fact that the radio waves show circular polarization is additional evidence that a magnetic field is present.

What is the distinction between a Type IVA burst and the microwave impulsive bursts that we discussed in the preceding section? The difference seems to hinge largely on the question of duration. As Wild has remarked, "In many cases the distinction between the two phases is at best a subjective one." If an impulsive burst evolves into a prolonged period of continuous emission, which may last up to two hours, then at least the latter stages are regarded as belonging to the Type IVA category.

The most spectacular and most distinctive of the Type IV events are those which begin at wavelengths in the meter range a few minutes after large Type II bursts have died away. In Fig. 5-11 we have again followed Kundu's simple chronological notation and labeled this region Type IVB. It was A. Boischot's identification of such events with the great Nancay grating interferometer that in fact led to the recognition of Type IV emission as a separate kind of solar phenomenon. In Fig. 5-12 we have reproduced one of Boischot's records, which shows a broad Type IVB source near the sun's western limb. At the same time

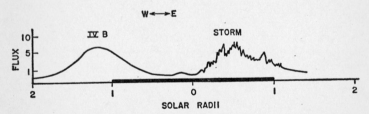

FIG. 5-12 A Type IVB burst and a noise storm shown as the sun drifted through one lobe of the Nancay interferometer on November 20, 1956. The instrument consists of 32 dishes spaced along a 1.55-km baseline; at its operating frequency of 169 Mc/sec it produces a beamwidth of 3.8' of arc. The visible disc of the sun is indicated by the heavy line. Flux density is expressed in units of 10^{-20} w/m^2/cps. (After A. Boischot.[9])

a *noise storm* was active near the eastern edge of the disc, but we shall have to postpone discussion of this kind of event until the next section.

As the figure indicates, Type IVB sources are very large, typically extending over a third of the diameter of the visible disc. However, it is their *motion* that really sets them apart from other kinds of Type IV events. Like Type II and Type III bursts, the Type IVB sources rise swiftly through the corona, displaying speeds up to 3000 km/sec and occasionally reaching altitudes of 5 solar radii before they finally come to rest and disappear from the radio records.

What is the physical nature of these vast, rapidly moving sources? Here again we seem to be dealing with a broad spectrum of frequencies, all of which come from a single region of the solar atmosphere at any given moment. As a result, most radio astronomers believe that this is yet another example of synchrotron emission, which in turn implies that a Type IVB source contains an enormous cloud of relativistic electrons. Calculations indicate that the electrons must have individual energies of about 3 Mev, and that no less than 4×10^{32} electrons can account for the observed maximum intensities. The electrons are almost certainly accompanied by equal numbers of the more massive positive ions, forming a plasma cloud that drags along with it a portion of the magnetic field from the immediate vicinity of the flare. It must be presumed that this "kidnapped" magnetic field quickly reshapes itself to form a *magnetic bottle* that moves along with the cloud and prevents the high-speed electrons from quickly diffusing away. At the same time, the imbedded magnetic flux supplies the field of about 1 gauss that is required to explain the observed synchrotron spectrum. Quite likely it is the "leakiness" of the magnetic bottle that limits the active lifetime of a Type IVB source to a period ranging from 10 minutes to 2 hours.

On occasion Type IVB emission seems to be followed by an entirely different kind of meter-wavelength event, which is (inevitably!) labeled IVC. Actually, there is some suspicion that the two phenomena may begin at about the same time, but the Type IVC component is not noticed until its competitor has died away. However that may be, Type IVC is distinguished by its longevity, which can extend to several days. Because of this great lifetime, and because the received flux density may rise to as much as 10^{-19} w/m²/cps, a Type IVC event is also known as a *continuum storm*. The radiation arises from a small, stationary source deep in the sun's atmosphere above the flare region, and it shows strong circular polarization. An added peculiarity is that the emission is rather sharply beamed in the vertical direction, so that we cannot receive it unless the source is near the center of the visible solar disc, where it is more or less "aimed" toward the earth. It is thought that the radiation is due to plasma waves excited by fast, flare-born electrons that have been trapped in the magnetic loops above sunspots. Oscillating back and forth along field lines, the electrons set up longitudinal waves in the surrounding plasma, and these waves in turn generate the observed radio emission.

Recapitulation. In an earlier section we reviewed the radio events that accompany a small flare. We now see that these same events characterize the early or flash phase of a large flare. Streams of electrons are shot into the corona to excite Type III radio bursts, with the debris later generating Type V continuous emission. Other flare-accelerated electrons plunge into the chromosphere, where they radiate microwave bursts and X-rays.

All of these processes depend upon the ability of the flare—large or small—to create swarms of very fast *electrons*. The additional factor that seems to distinguish a large flare is its explosive ejection of a cloud of *plasma*, a material far more massive than the ethereal streams of electrons. It is as if a volcano, after being content to emit showers of sparks and ashes, suddenly got down to business and began to belch forth a torrent of lava. The plasma eruption apparently generates a shock wave that races outward through the corona at supersonic speeds, exciting Type II bursts as it goes (Fig. 5-13). Behind the shock front trails the plasma cloud with an imbedded magnetic field that has been torn away from the solar surface. Whirling about within the cloud, relativistic electrons emit synchrotron radiation, which is observed as a moving Type IVB burst. Other electrons, left behind near the flare site, continue to generate Type

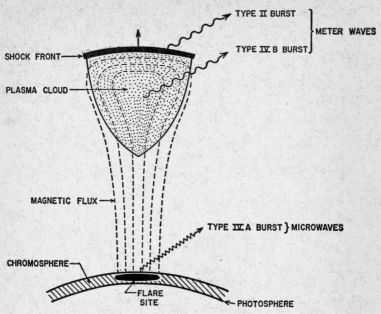

FIG. 5-13   Schematic drawing of the second phase of a large flare.

IVA microwave emission through the synchrotron process. Possibly the long-lived Type IVC radiation, which rings down the curtain on the performance, is maintained by electrons that slowly leak out of the dying plasma cloud only to be funneled back to the flare site by the stretched magnetic field lines.

NOISE STORMS

The great outburst of radio noise that jammed the British radars in 1942 and led Stanley Hey to the discovery of solar radio emission (Chapter 1) was what we now call a *noise storm*. Radiation of this type is found only at wavelengths in excess of a meter, but in that region of the spectrum it constitutes by far the greatest part of the observed nonthermal solar radio flux. Near the time of sunspot maximum, noise storms are in progress about 10% of the time, and during a period of intense activity hundreds of storm bursts may occur each hour. Individual storms generally last from a few hours to several days, with the intensity of the received flux rising as high as 1000 times that of the quiet sun.

In most cases storm radiation is a mixture of two quite distinct components. There is a background of broad-band, relatively steady emission and then, superimposed on this continuum, are large numbers of short bursts designated as *Type I* or "storm" bursts. Whereas the continuum sprawls across frequency bands of 100 Mc/sec or more, the bursts have bandwidths of only about 2% of their center frequencies—that is, a burst occurring at 200 Mc/sec will be confined to a band of perhaps 4 Mc/sec. Figure 5-14 shows a number of these storm bursts, which

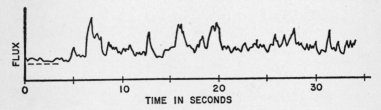

FIG. 5-14 Noise storm radiation at 200 Mc/sec on October 12, 1957. The dashed line indicates a flux level 4 times that of the quiet sun. (After A. D. Fokker.)

typically last from less than a tenth of a second to several seconds. Some astronomers have suggested that the bursts and the background continuum may be one and the same thing, with the background being merely the superposition of myriads of small bursts. However, the evidence tends to favor the view that we are actually dealing with two separate phenomena.

In Fig. 5-12 we saw a noise storm as it appeared to the great Nancay interferometer. Instruments such as this show that the storm emission originates in local regions high in the corona above sunspot groups—in fact, storm centers develop above two-thirds of *all* groups that include at least one prominent spot. The diameters of the storms ordinarily range from 4' to 10' of arc, but the individual bursts come from far smaller sources scattered about within these regions. Since storm centers often radiate for several days, their altitudes, like those of the radio plages, can be determined from the speed with which they appear to move across the visible disc of the sun. The measured heights are large, ranging from 0.2 to 1 solar radius, and as might be expected at these great altitudes, the radio sources seldom lie directly above the associated sunspots.

Emission from a noise storm is beamed in the vertical direction, a property shared with Type IVC bursts. Thus storm radiation is received with full intensity only when the source is near the center of the visible disc, with the emission cone pointed toward the earth. Some idea of the sharpness of this beaming can be gained from the fact that the 169 Mc/sec flux drops to half of its maximum value when the source is roughly 40° from the center of the disc. Curiously enough, the stronger the storm, the narrower the radiation cone appears to be.

Both the background continuum and the Type I bursts are circularly polarized in a sense that seems to depend on the solar hemisphere in which the storm is found. When R. Payne-Scott and A. G. Little first made such measurements in 1950, they found that storms *south* of the solar equator usually produced emission polarized in the right-hand sense, whereas radiation from storm centers *north* of the equator displayed left-hand polarization. It is remarkable, and of course highly significant, that when the next solar cycle came along this relationship was completely reversed! The reader may recall that an analogous reversal occurs in the magnetic polarities of sunspots (Chapter 2), emphasizing once more the intimate relationship between the radio phenomena and solar magnetic fields.

What causes a solar noise storm? Since storms are relatively common phenomena of the disturbed sun and have been extensively observed, it is rather surprising to find that there is no generally accepted theory of the emission process. This does not mean that there are *no* theories, but rather that there are too many theories and not enough facts of the right kind to distinguish between them! Such a situation is quite common in new and rapidly growing fields of science, where it is easy for a worker's imagination to outrun his data.

We can immediately dismiss thermal radiation, for the observed brightness temperatures soar as high as 10^{10} ° K, some

10,000 times greater than the measured coronal temperatures. Noise storms appear to be associated in some way with flares, since 80 to 90% of the storms follow a flare by 2 hours or less. In some instances noise storms seem to evolve from extended periods of Type IVC emission, which we have found to be part of the aftermath of a large flare.

The noted French radio astronomer J. F. Denisse believes that storm radiation results from plasma waves. According to this picture, flare-generated particles are trapped and temporarily stored in magnetic fields high in the corona. Over a period of hours or days the particles slowly escape from their imperfect prison and stream back toward the solar surface, following magnetic tubes such as we see in Fig. 5-13. As the particles re-enter the denser portions of the corona, they excite downward-moving plasma waves, and these in turn generate radio waves traveling in the same direction—that is, toward the photosphere. If this hypothesis is correct, then the radiation that we receive must be a *reflection* from a lower level of the corona where the critical frequency equals the wave frequency. The reader may recognize similarities between Denisse's theory and certain of the mechanisms proposed for Type IV emission.

A. M. Malinge has suggested an ingenious variation of this theory that explains both the Type I bursts and the continuum. According to Malinge, a storm center radiates outward as well as inward. The energy that is beamed away from the sun is received directly, and it is this component that we recognize as the relatively steady, continuous background. The other component must, as in Denisse's theory, be reflected from a lower layer before it can escape from the corona. Malinge pictures the reflecting layer as being in a constant state of turmoil, so that we perceive in it an image of the real source that is subject to large and rapid fluctuations, like the dancing, scintillating reflections of sunlight from water waves. It is of course these violent fluctuations that appear as the Type I storm bursts.

While these theories are undoubtedly attractive, a number of other radio astronomers have suggested that noise storms may result from gyromagnetic emission, rather than from plasma waves. The synchrotron process might account for the broad continuum, but it is poorly adapted to explaining the very narrow-band Type I bursts. In general, gyromagnetic theories experience a problem in accounting for the observed intensities of noise storms, and the authors of these theories have usually resorted either to *electron bunching* or to *wave amplification* in order to overcome this difficulty. If the gyrating electrons are grouped in "bunches" of N electrons, then they radiate in unison and the resulting signal is stronger than that of a single electron by a factor of N^2, rather than merely N. Wave amplification is achieved (theoretically) by allowing an initially weak radio wave to interact with energetic electrons in the corona in such a way that part of the kinetic energy of the electrons is transferred to the wave, increasing its intensity. The mechanisms that produce electron bunching and wave amplification are necessarily somewhat involved, and they of course add considerable complexity to theories of noise storms that rely upon them. But by this time the reader has undoubtedly concluded that the entire subject of radio emission from the disturbed sun is one of challenging complexity!

FLARE STARS

We have seen that the active sun is a powerful radio transmitter. Should we expect, then, to detect similar outbursts from other stars? Calculations suggest that the very strongest solar bursts might be barely detectable if the sun were at the distance of the nearer stars. In 1958 Sir Bernard Lovell began to monitor certain nearby stars with the famous 250-ft radio telescope at Jodrell Bank. He concentrated his attention on a few peculiar "red dwarf" stars known as *UV Ceti* or *flare* stars, since these objects were known to emit brief flashes of light on a time scale not unlike that of a solar flare.

The search paid off handsomely in 1960, when both Lovell and the Australians O. B. Slee and C. S. Higgins detected brief bursts of radio noise that were almost simultaneous with the optical brightenings.[10,11] It was immediately obvious that the flare stars emit radio energy on a scale that makes the sun seem puny by comparison, for a stellar radio outburst may represent as much as a million times the energy of the most powerful solar events! At present two distinct types of stellar bursts have been identified—one that resembles a solar noise storm and another that is similar to a Type II burst. It is intriguing to speculate that one day we may be able to trace cycles of activity in other stars as we now do for the sun. Certainly there is every reason to expect that new generations of increasingly powerful radio telescopes will contribute in an important way to our understanding of myriad stars both like and unlike the sun.

REFERENCES

1. Allen, C. W., *Astrophysical Quantities* (University of London, 1963), pp. 187-189.
2. Wild, J. P., Smerd, S. F., and Weiss, A. A., "Solar Bursts," in *Annual Review of Astronomy and Astrophysics*, Vol. 1, edited by L. Goldberg (Annual Reviews, Inc., Palo Alto, 1963), pp. 291-366.
3. Kundu, M. R., *Solar Radio Astronomy* (John Wiley & Sons, Inc., New York, 1965), pp. 168-170.
4. Covington, A. E. and Medd, W. J., "Variations of the Daily Level of the 10.7-Centimetre Solar Emission," J. Roy. Astron. Soc. Canada 48, 136-149 (1954).
5. Christiansen, W. N. and Warburton, J. A., "The Distribution of Radio Brightness Over the Solar Disk at a Wavelength of 21 Centimeters," Australian J. Phys. 6, 190-202 (1953).
6. Covington, A. E., "Solar Emission at 10-Cm Wavelength," in *Paris Symposium on Radio Astronomy*, edited by R. N. Bracewell (Stanford University Press, Stanford, California, 1959), pp. 159-165.
7. Wild, J. P., Sheridan, K. V., and Neylan, A. A., "An Investigation of the Speed of the Solar Disturbances Responsible for Type III Radio Bursts," Australian J. Phys. 12, 369-398 (1959).
8. Weiss, A. A., "The Positions and Movements of the Sources of Solar Radio Bursts of Spectral Type II," Australian J. Phys. 16, 240-271 (1963).
9. Boischot, A., "Caracteres d'un Type d'Emission Hertzienne Associe a Certaines Eruptiones Chromospheriques," Compt. Rend. 244, 1326-1329 (1957).
10. Lovell, Sir Bernard, "Radio-emitting Flare Stars," Sci. Am. 211, 13-19 (August, 1964).
11. Slee, O. B., Higgins, C. S., and Patston, G. E., "Visual and Radio Observations of Flare Stars," Sky and Telescope 25, 83-86 (1963).

FOR FURTHER READING

Cowling, T. G., *Magnetohydrodynamics* (Interscience Publishers, Inc., New York, 1957).

Hess, W. N., editor, *The Physics of Solar Flares* (U.S. Government Printing Office, Washington, 1964).

Odishaw, H., editor, *Research in Geophysics* (The M.I.T. Press, Cambridge, Massachusetts, 1964), Vol. 1, Chapters 1, 2, 3.

Smith, H. J. and Smith, E. v. P., *Solar Flares* (The Macmillan Co., New York, 1963).

Spitzer, L., *Physics of Fully Ionized Gases* (Interscience Publishers, Inc., New York, 1956).

Wild, J. P., "The Radio Emission of the Sun," in *Radio Astronomy Today*, edited by H. P. Palmer, R. D. Davies, and M. I. Large (Manchester University Press, Manchester, 1963).

Solar System Radio Astronomy, edited by J. Aarons (Plenum Press, New York, 1965), Chapters 7-12.

6   *In the Moon's Shadow*

"Where there is much light, the shadows are deepest."

GOETHE

"Now as concerning natural Eclipses of the Sun and Moon, they oftentimes portend great Changes and Revolutions which shall happen in Empires and Kingdoms, as well as Misfortunes to particular Persons. . . ." Written in January of 1720 in a London journal, these doleful words reflected the popular superstitions of the day.[1] Continuing in the same vein, the writer proceeded to prove his point by offering a bill of particulars. "Observe the fatal Effects of Eclipses by what follows. *Anno Mundi* 3180 * an Eclipse of the Sun happen'd, at which Time the Kingdom of *Israel* began to decline. . . . In 3469 an Eclipse of the Sun happen'd, after which *Xerxes* was overcome at *Salamine*. In 3519 so great an Eclipse of the Sun happen'd that the Stars were seen at Noon; and shortly after the *Peloponesian* War broke out with the *Athenians*. . . . In 59 (A.D.) an Eclipse of the Sun preceded *Nero's* most cruel Persecution of the *Christians*. . . . In 812 an Eclipse of the Sun preceded the Death of *Charles* the Great. . . ." In all, the writer listed 18 historic calamities, each of which had occurred a short time after an eclipse!

HOW DOES IT HAPPEN?

Despite the widespread fear that accompanied eclipses until recent times, the astronomical cause of the phenomenon was understood by scholars in antiquity. It is even possible that the great ruins at Stonehenge, England, are the remains of a kind of

---

* *Anno Mundi*, or "year of the world," refers to a calendar dating from the supposed creation of the world in the year 4004 B.C. Thus *Anno Mundi* 3180 is actually 824 B.C.

analog computer used as early as 1500 B.C. for predicting eclipses.[2] As usual, however, the popular superstitions persisted until scientific education had touched the masses.

Figure 6-1 shows the circumstances of a *solar eclipse,* in which

FIG. 6-1 Woodcut diagram of a solar eclipse from one of the earliest printed textbooks on astronomy, the *Opus Sphericum* of Sacrobosco. We see the tip of the moon's shadow falling on the earth (symbolized by a globe with a castle), while the shadow of the earth itself extends off to the right. The figure is from the edition of 1501, but the book existed in manuscript form in the 13th century.

the moon passes between the earth and the sun. The other kind of eclipse—a *lunar eclipse*—occurs when the moon passes through the shadow of the earth. Since the figure was drawn long before Copernicus had placed the sun in its proper position at the center of the solar system, it emphasizes the fact that the understanding and prediction of eclipses does not depend upon any special system of cosmology.

The earth moves about the sun in a plane known as the *plane of the ecliptic.* It is easy to see that if the moon circled the earth in this same plane we should have a solar eclipse at each "new" moon and a lunar eclipse at each "full" moon. Actually, as Fig. 6-2 shows, the moon's orbit is tilted with respect to the ecliptic plane, so that an eclipse can take place only if new moon or full moon occurs when the moon is near a node of its orbit—that is, near one of the two points at which the lunar orbit intersects the ecliptic. Because of this restriction, we can enjoy a maximum of seven eclipses per year, either five of the sun and two of the moon or four of the sun and three of the moon. In some years

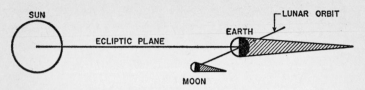

FIG. 6-2 The tilt of the moon's orbit. Here we are looking "edge on" at the orbits of both the moon and the earth. The diagram is not to scale, and the actual angle between the two orbital planes is only 5°.

only two eclipses occur, both of which are of the sun. It is important to note that a lunar eclipse is visible to half of the earth's population (if the weather cooperates!). On the other hand, since the tip of the moon's shadow at best barely reaches the earth, a solar eclipse can be seen only by the fortunate few who live in the narrow track of the shadow as it races across our globe. Of course, many outside of the eclipse zone may behold a *partial* eclipse in which the sun's disc is not completely hidden.

Astronomers long have mounted costly and time-consuming expeditions to remote corners of the globe to record the brief moments of totality of a solar eclipse. In fact, old-timers are wont to recount their careers in terms of "eclipses I have seen." What is it that makes such efforts worth while, even though a few capricious clouds may at the last moment cause all to end in disaster?

It is one of the curious coincidences of nature that the relative sizes and distances of the sun and the moon are such that they subtend nearly equal angles in the sky. Of course, the distances vary slightly, and sometimes we have an *annular* eclipse in which the moon does not completely cover the sun—or, to put it a little differently, the tip of the lunar shadow falls slightly short of the earth's surface. Often, however, the moon serves as an ideal screen to cut off the overwhelming glare of the photosphere, which normally hides the sun's atmosphere. Until relatively recent times, it was only during the fleeting moments of a total eclipse that such important features as the chromosphere, the prominences, and the corona could be detected at all. The modern instruments described in Chapter 2 have largely removed this limitation, and today solar physics is less crucially dependent upon eclipse data. Still, there are certain observations that can be made only during an eclipse. These include delineation of the faint outer corona and the photography of star fields surrounding the sun in a continuing search for the light-bending that is one of the few direct observational tests of relativity theory. According to the theory, light rays passing near a massive body must be deflected slightly, and thus stars near the solar limb should appear to be shifted about 1.75 sec of arc from their normal positions. Unfortunately, this displacement is so small as to be at the limit of detectability.[3]

RADIO OBSERVATIONS OF SOLAR ECLIPSES

Since eclipse records proved to be of such importance in the optical study of the sun, it is scarcely surprising that radio astronomers wasted little time in turning to this technique. The pioneers were R. H. Dicke and R. Beringer, who used 1.25-cm radar receiving equipment to observe a partial eclipse at Cambridge, Massachusetts, on July 9, 1945. Since that date, radio telescopes of all kinds have been directed at dozens of solar eclipses. The early experimenters foresaw the possibility of using the edge of the moon to isolate individual solar radio features, thereby increasing enormously the very limited resolving power then available. To a certain extent these hopes have been realized, although the usefulness of the technique has been restricted by complications that could scarcely have been anticipated. Then, too, advances in instrumentation have, as in the optical case, tended to reduce reliance on eclipse data.

What does a radio telescope "see" when it looks at an eclipse of the sun? As might be expected, the radio flux behaves much like the visible light, decreasing throughout the initial stages of the eclipse and reaching a minimum at totality. Figure 6-3 is an eclipse record made by the French radio astronomer, M. Laffineur and his colleagues. Notice that even at totality there is a residual flux I_r of about 15%. Why should this be? If the reader will recall that at most wavelengths the radio sun is much *larger* than the optical sun, the explanation is simple. Except at the very shortest wavelengths, radio eclipses are always annular—

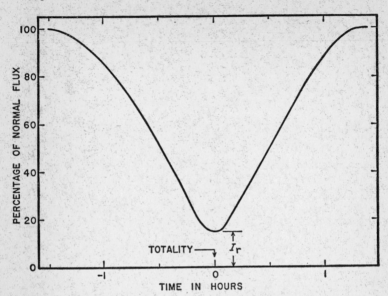

FIG. 6-3 Eclipse curve obtained at 545 Mc/sec ($\lambda = 55$ cm) on June 30, 1954. The radio telescope was a 20-ft parabolic dish, in which the sun appeared as an unresolved point source. (After M. Laffineur, P. Coupiac, and B. Vauquois.[4])

that is, the moon can hide only a portion of the effective radio disc.

Since the size of this disc increases with wavelength, we would expect the residual flux to increase in a similar manner, and such is indeed the case. Figure 6-4 compares eclipse curves made at very short and very long wavelengths. At 8 mm, I_r is only 0.5%, but at 2.73 m it amounts to nearly 50%! Does the latter figure mean that the moon can cover only half the area of the 2.73 m radio sun? This is correct insofar as we can assume that the solar radio disc is of uniform brightness. If we let D_e represent the angular diameter of this presumed uniform disc, while D_m is the angular diameter of the moon, it is easy to see that

$$I_r = 100 \, \frac{\pi(D_e/2)^2 - \pi(D_m/2)^2}{\pi(D_e/2)^2} = 100 \, \frac{D_e^2 - D_m^2}{D_e^2}. \quad (6\text{-}1)$$

During the eclipse of February 15, 1961, the Soviet astronomer Alekseev and his associates measured I_r at no less than 14 dif-

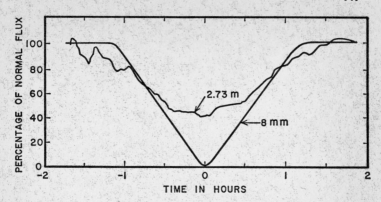

FIG. 6-4 Eclipse curves for wavelengths of 8 mm (after J. P. Hagen[5]) and 2.73 m (after Yu. I. Alekseev et al.[6]).

ferent wavelengths, and they then used Eq. (6-1) to find D_e. In Fig. 6-5, where we see the results of this experiment, the steady "growth" of the radio sun with wavelength is strikingly evident.

Of course, the assumption of uniform brightness over the en-

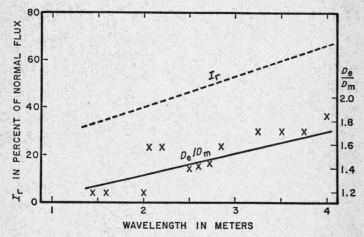

FIG. 6-5 The dashed line shows the increase in residual flux I_r with wavelength for the eclipse of February 15, 1961. The solid line shows the increase in the computed diameter D_e of the solar radio disc relative to the diameter of the moon or the optical sun. Values of D_e/D_m derived from the duration of the eclipse are indicated by crosses. (After Yu. I. Alekseev et al.[6])

tire solar radio disc is merely a rough approximation, as is clear from Fig. 4-7. Consequently, D_e is only an "effective" diameter whose physical significance must be interpreted with some caution. Still another clue to the diameter of the radio sun is provided by the *duration* of an eclipse, for it is obvious that the moon will take longer to cross a large disc than it will to cross a small one. Notice, for example, that the 2.73 m eclipse in Fig. 6-4 lasted considerably longer than the 8 mm event. In their study of the 1961 eclipse the Russian astronomers took advantage of this effect to make a second set of measurements of the diameter of the solar radio disc, and the results are shown as crosses in Fig. 6-5.

In Chapter 4 we saw that the outline of the radio sun is elliptical, rather than circular. Actually, the first suggestion of this flattening came from eclipse observations made as early as 1947. Let us refer to Fig. 6-6 to see how this ellipticity reveals itself in

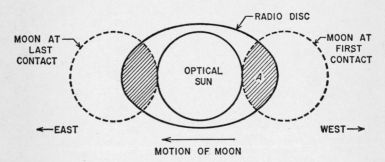

FIG. 6-6   Eclipse of the elliptical disc of the radio sun.

the eclipse curve. At the moment of first *optical* contact between the sun and the moon, the shaded area A of the radio disc has been eclipsed. Now, it is not at all difficult to see that this area is greater than it would have been had the radio outline been circular, and of course a similar situation exists at the time of final optical contact. As a result, during both the early and late phases of the eclipse the observed flux is less than would have been the case for a circular disc.

A little thought will show that solar limb brightening should affect the slope of the eclipse curve in a similar manner, and thus the detailed shape of the curve might enable us to deduce the distribution of brightness across the radio sun. During the eclipse of June 30, 1954, successful investigations of this kind were made at wavelengths near 10 cm by F. T. Haddock and A. E. Covington, and at 8.6 mm by J. P. Hagen and R. J. Coates. Unfortunately, two difficulties have seriously limited the usefulness of the method at longer wavelengths. First, the eclipse curve is comparatively insensitive to the details of the brightness distribution because the moon hides only a fraction of the total radio sun. Second, if the sun is at all active, variable radio flux from localized sources may completely confuse the picture. As a result of these problems, high-resolution interferometry has proven to be a more powerful technique for mapping the quiet sun.

We have just remarked that eclipse observations may be complicated by the presence on the solar disc of local sources of radio noise—for example, radio plages or noise storms. Scientists, however, are ingenious people, and it soon occurred to them that they might turn a seeming disadvantage into an advantage by using the eclipse data to study the sources themselves. As might be expected, when a strong source is covered by the moon the eclipse curve dips sharply; when the source is uncovered the curve shows an abrupt rise. With the aid of Fig. 6-7 we can see that *both* observations are necessary if we are to make an unambiguous determination of the location of the source S. At

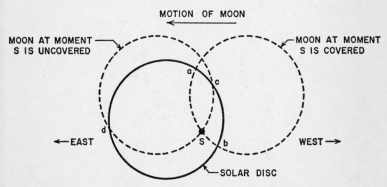

FIG. 6-7 Location of a localized radio source S through eclipse observations. Notice that the method works even though the eclipse is only partial.

the moment the moon covers the source the received flux drops, but this tells us only that S lies somewhere along the dashed arc *ab*. When the moon reaches the left-hand position in the figure the flux increases, indicating that S also lies on the dashed arc *cd*. It is evident, then, that the source must be located at the *intersection* of the two arcs.

Although eclipse data made a historical contribution to the mapping of solar radio sources, it takes little imagination to see that the interpretation of the observations might become impossibly complex if many sources were present, or if the flux from one or more sources showed rapid time variations. Some of the ambiguities can be resolved by recording the same eclipse at several widely separated sites, but once again the development of high-resolution instruments has tended to supplant the eclipse technique.

Perhaps the future of eclipse observations lies in combining the two methods—that is, in using a narrow-beam radio telescope to watch a single source during an eclipse. In this way the location and even the size of the source can be pinpointed with an accuracy greatly exceeding the resolving power of the instrument itself. For example, during the eclipse of February 15, 1961, J. P. Castelli and his associates measured solar source diameters as small as 45″ of arc with a radio telescope whose beamwidth was nearly 2°! The sizes of the sources were inferred from the time required for the limb of the moon to cover or uncover them.[7]

In principle, the precision of this method is limited only by the *diffraction* or spreading of radio waves that occurs at the lunar limb. An entirely analogous phenomenon is observed in optics when wavefronts of light from a point source are interrupted by a straightedge, as in Fig. 6-8. Because of the wave nature of light, the edge of the shadow is not a simple sharp line, but a pattern of bright and dark fringes that can be observed on a suitable screen. In the radioastronomical case the straightedge is replaced by a short arc of the moon's limb, while the surface of the earth serves as a screen. We can simulate the motion of the moon by imagining that the straightedge is moving upward in the figure, in which case it is evident that the shadow pattern will sweep across the screen in the same direction. (Depending

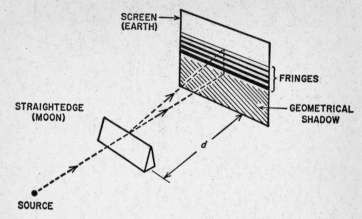

FIG. 6-8 Diffraction pattern produced by a straightedge. The scale of the fringes is greatly exaggerated.

upon the circumstances of the eclipse, the lunar shadow races over the earth at speeds ranging from 1800 to 8400 km/hour!) Clearly, if there were a fixed radio telescope in the plane of the screen it would record a series of maxima and minima as the shadow passed over it, and it would be impossible to fix a precise moment at which the source had been eclipsed. In effect, the neat arcs ab and cd of Fig. 6-7 must be replaced by "fuzzy" arcs, thereby introducing a corresponding uncertainty into the measured position of the source S.

How serious is this limitation? Optical experience indicates that resolving power is related to the scale of the diffraction pattern in the image being studied. In the earth-moon system, the fringes that sweep across the earth are spaced at intervals of roughly $\sqrt{d\lambda}$, where d is the distance from the earth to the moon and λ is the wavelength of the radiation. If we let $\lambda = 1$ m and take d equal to its average value of 3.84×10^5 km, we find the fringe interval to be of the order of 20 km. Now, as viewed from the moon, the *angle* subtended by this interval is $\sqrt{d\lambda}/d = \sqrt{\lambda/d} \cong 5 \times 10^{-5}$ rad or 10″ of arc. This value establishes an order of magnitude for the theoretical angular precision of eclipse measurements made at a wavelength of 1 m.

Eclipses are not restricted to the sun and the moon. For example, as the moon glides through the skies it passes in front of numerous stars, galaxies, nebulae, and even an occasional planet. However, astronomers prefer to speak of such events as *occultations*, rather than "eclipses." The mapping of distant radio galaxies shows promise of settling the ultimate cosmological question of the overall structure of the universe, and scientists are now beginning to take advantage of occultations to pinpoint the positions of these galaxies with unprecedented precision. In the past even the largest interferometers have often been unable to locate a radio galaxy with sufficient accuracy to permit it to be identified unambiguously with one of the myriad optical images that crowd long-exposure photographs.

Figure 6-9 shows a pioneering observation by the Australian

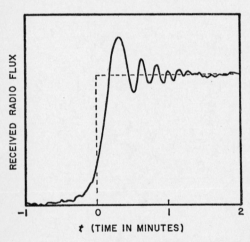

FIG. 6-9 Diffraction fringes produced by the emergence of a small radio source from behind the lunar limb. In the absence of diffraction the source would have emerged almost instantly at $t = 0$, with the flux following the dashed line; i.e., $t = 0$ marks the edge of the "geometrical shadow." The data were recorded at 410 Mc/sec with a 210-ft parabolic dish. (After C. Hazard, M. B. Mackey, and A. J. Shimmins.[8])

C. Hazard and his colleagues of an occultation of the remote *quasi-stellar radio source* 3C273. By using all the information contained in this beautifully defined fringe pattern, the Australian scientists were able to locate 3C273 with an estimated accuracy of about 1″ of arc. It is even possible to infer the angular diameter of the object with similar precision from the shapes of the fringes. The method is quite analogous to determining the size of a source from the "visibility" of its fringes in a radio interferometer (see Chapter 3). If the source is extended, we can regard it as being made up of a great number of individual point sources, each of which generates its own fringe pattern. The observed pattern is thus a smeared composite, whose fringe amplitude is diminished in a way that can be related mathematically to the angular extent of the object. Strangely enough, eclipse techniques originally inspired by man's curiosity about the nearby sun are now being used to probe the utmost depths of the universe!

REFERENCES

1. The Delphick Oracle (J. Roberts, London, January, 1720), pp. 24-27.
2. Hawkins, G. S., "Stonehenge Decoded," Nature 200, 306-308 (1963).
3. Kluber, H. von, "The Determination of Einstein's Light Deflection in the Gravitational Field of the Sun," in *Vistas in Astronomy*, Vol. 3, edited by A. Beer (Pergamon Press, Ltd., London, 1960), pp. 47-77.
4. Laffineur, M., Coupiac, P., and Vauquois, B., "Observations Radioelectriques de l'Eclipse de 30 juin 1954," in *Solar Eclipses and the Ionosphere*, edited by W. J. G. Beynon and G. M. Brown (Pergamon Press, Ltd., London, 1956), pp. 261- 263.
5. Hagen, J. P., "Radial Brightness Distribution of the Sun at 8 Mm," in *Solar Eclipses and the Ionosphere, loc. cit.*, pp. 253-257.
6. Alekseev, Yu.I., Babii, V. I., Vitkevich, V. V., Gorelova, M. V., and Sukhovei, A. G., "Observations of the Solar Radio Emission on Meter Wavelengths During the Total Solar Eclipse of February 15, 1961," Soviet Astron.—AJ 6, 504-510 (1963).
7. Castelli, J. P., Cohen, Helen, Straka, R. M., and Aarons, J., "Radio Measurements of Two Total Eclipses," Icarus 2, 317-328 (1963).
8. Hazard, C., Mackey, M. B., and Shimmins, A. J., "Investigation of the Radio Source 3C273 by the Method of Lunar Occultations," Nature 197, 1037-1039 (1963).

FOR FURTHER READING

Castelli, J. P. and Aarons, J., "A Survey of Radio Observations of Solar Eclipses," in *Solar System Radio Astronomy*, edited by J. Aarons (Plenum Press, Inc., New York, 1965), pp. 49-79.

Hazard, C., "The Structure of the Extra-Galactic Radio Sources," in *Quasi-Stellar Sources and Gravitational Collapse,* edited by I. Robinson, A. Schild, and E. L. Schucking (University of Chicago Press, Chicago, 1965), pp. 135-157.

Scheuer, P. A. G., "On the Use of Lunar Occultations for Investigating the Angular Structure of Radio Sources," Australian J. Phys. 15, 333-343 (1962).

Scheuer, P. A. G., "Radio Structure of 3C273 and Spectra of Radio Sources," in *Quasi-Stellar Sources and Gravitational Collapse, loc. cit.,* pp. 373-380.

7 Echoes from the Sun

"It is more blessed to give than to receive."
ACTS

More than any other kind of scientist, the astronomer has been confined to the role of a pure observer. The very nature of his work has made it impossible for him to perform controlled experiments like those carried on in the laboratories of the chemist and the physicist. Indeed, it is a remarkable tribute to human ingenuity that the astronomer has been able to learn so much merely by studying the radiation from distant sources over whose environment he has no control.

In recent years two exciting developments have offered the astronomer a chance to become a real "experimentalist." One such development, of course, is the dawning of the "space age," during which scientists will be able to probe, explore, and sample nearby astronomical bodies much as the geologists and the geophysicists have already done for the earth. The other development is the successful contacting by radar of a number of bodies in the solar system. When he uses radar the astronomer can drop his purely passive role, and for the first time *control* the radiation he is studying. He can predetermine its direction, its timing, its frequency, its intensity, its duration, and its polarization. Although most people equate radar with finding only the distance and direction of a target, we shall see that it is also capable of providing a surprising amount of information about movement and rotation, the nature of the reflecting surface, and the properties of any atmosphere that may surround the target.

An earlier volume of this series outlined in some detail the general history and technique of radar astronomy.[1] We shall not repeat that material here, but shall instead confine ourselves to the specific question of what we can learn about the sun itself through the radar method.

FIRST CONTACT

The first serious discussion of the possibility of establishing radar contact with the sun appears to have been published in 1952 by the Australian radio astronomer F. J. Kerr.[2] At that time extraterrestrial echoes had been obtained only from the moon and from meteorites entering the earth's own atmosphere. Kerr's paper was appropriately entitled "On the Possibility of Obtaining Radar Echoes from the Sun and Planets," and after a lengthy consideration of the kind of equipment that would be required, he concluded that "the detection of sun echoes appears technically possible, but a radio-engineering project of considerable magnitude is involved."

That the project was indeed "of considerable magnitude" is evidenced by the fact that seven years were to elapse before a successful experiment was conducted! Finally, in April of 1959, V. R. Eshleman, R. C. Barthle, and P. B. Gallagher of Stanford University obtained the first real evidence of a solar radar echo.[3] They used an array of four large diamond-shaped rhombic antennas that extended over an area of 725 × 800 ft. Actually, the array had been erected for a quite different purpose and its principal beam was pointed east at an elevation of 10° above the horizon. It was only when the sun rose almost due east that it passed through the beam at all. This occurred during a period of a few days near the equinoxes in the spring and fall, at which times the radar experiment could be attempted for about 30 minutes each morning.

For the transmission phase of such an experiment, the antenna was connected to a 40-kw transmitter that operated at a frequency of 25.6 Mc/sec. The transmitter was alternately switched on and off at intervals of 30 sec, producing what in radar parlance is termed a *pulse length* of 30 sec, a far cry from the microsecond pulses ordinarily used in military radars. Transmission was continued for 15 minutes, which is a little less than the time required for a signal to reach the sun and return. Then, just before the first signals were due back at the earth, the transmitter was turned off and the antenna was connected to a sensitive receiving system to begin a period of listening for the hoped-for echoes. The whole performance was a good deal like the man who "hollers" in a canyon and then cups his hand to his ear to await the echo.

It must not be thought that the solar echo could simply be displayed as a "blip" on a cathode ray screen, as is commonly done in terrestrial radars. Both theory and experiment indicated that the solar signal was no less than 44 decibels* *weaker* than the background noise in the system! Under these circumstances the signal could be separated from the noise only by subjecting a tape recording of the listening period to an elaborate statistical analysis performed by an electronic computer. Successful recovery of a signal in the face of such odds is possible largely because the analyst knows beforehand that the signal bears an artificially impressed periodicity; this, of course, emphasizes the advantage that the experimenter enjoys when he is able to control the characteristics of the radiation.

The Stanford scientists concluded that their analysis had shown that the odds were more than 100,000 to 1 that they had actually received solar echoes on three mornings in April of 1959. An earlier attempt near the autumnal equinox of 1958 apparently produced inconclusive results, while a later effort in the fall of 1959 was doomed by equipment failures. As the three experimenters themselves recognized, "The scientific information about the sun gained from the first radar experiments . . . is very limited." Quite properly, however, they pointed out that because of their success, "It is now possible to plan with confidence the systems and test procedures needed for more meaningful studies of our dynamic sun."

THE PROBLEM

Why is it that the sun is such a difficult radar target? After all, it has the same angular size as the moon, and one might therefore suppose that it should reflect just as much energy. In his pioneering paper, Kerr pointed out that it is true that the sun

---

* Decibels are widely used in electronics to express power ratios. The ratio in db is equal to 10 times the common logarithm of the actual power ratio. Thus 44 db is equivalent to a power ratio of about 25,000 to 1.

and the moon intercept about the same fraction of the *transmitted* radar pulse. However, the *reflected* signal from the sun has to travel 400 times as far to get back to the earth, and since the echo diverges and spreads as it goes, the usual inverse square law comes into play. As a result, the distance factor alone causes the solar echo to be 160,000 times, or 52 db, weaker than the signal returned by the moon!

A further loss may occur because the sun is a "soft" target. Instead of being reflected at a recognizable "hard" surface, as in the case of the moon, solar echoes are returned from an ill-defined layer in a turbulent atmosphere of gradually increasing density. During its round trip through the outer layers of this gaseous envelope, the radar signal may suffer serious absorption, especially since its path length can be increased appreciably by refraction. Figure 7-1 shows the paths followed by 38 Mc/sec rays

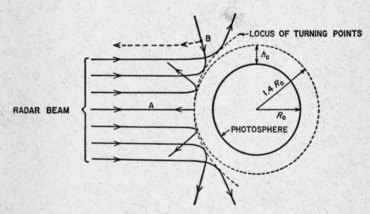

FIG. 7-1 Computed paths of 38 Mc/sec rays in the solar atmosphere. The dashed circle marks the critical height h_c at which the index of refraction becomes zero for this frequency. Except for the central ray A, the "turning points" of all the rays lie above the critical height. (After J. C. James.[4])

that were initially directed toward different portions of the solar disc. It is assumed that in general the rays are reflected by being scattered from small irregularities in the corona. Notice that a ray scattered at a point such as *B* may return to the earth via two routes, one of which is represented by the dashed line while the other involves retracing the inbound path. Energy scattered in directions other than these two is lost from the antenna beam and consequently cannot contribute to the echo unless it happens to be scattered a second time. (In connection with earlier chapters, it is of interest to note that radiation *emitted* at the point B also has the same choice of paths if it is to reach an antenna on the earth.)

Kerr suggested that in designing a solar radar the higher frequencies should be avoided for several reasons.[2] First, since such signals would penetrate deep into the solar atmosphere before being reflected, they would suffer disastrous attenuation. Second, we have seen that the radio sun is actually smaller at high frequencies, and would thus present a less effective target. Finally, it was evident that the competing thermal radio noise emitted by even the "quiet" sun would tend to drown out the feeble radar echo, and such noise of course increases with frequency. On the other hand, one cannot afford to lower the frequency so far that interference from the terrestrial ionosphere becomes important. After weighing all of the factors that are involved, Kerr concluded that frequencies of 25 to 30 Mc/sec should represent the best possible compromise. Seven years later this prediction was justified when, as we have described above, the first successful radar contact was made at a frequency of 25.6 Mc/sec.

It is useful to summarize the overall efficiency of the sun as a reflector by assigning to it a *radar cross section σ*. According to the usual definition, σ is the cross-sectional area of a perfectly isotropic scatterer which, if placed at the position of the sun, would return the same echo power to the antenna as does the sun itself. By a "perfectly isotropic scatterer" we mean a target that reflects the incident radar beam equally in all directions. In practice this ideal is approached by a smooth metal sphere whose radius r is large compared with the wavelength λ of the radiation; obviously the radar cross section of such a sphere is not far from $\sigma = \pi r^2$. Since the solar echo is believed to result largely from a scattering process, it seems reasonable to suppose that the sun will behave as a *rough* sphere, rather than as a smooth one. Now, σ for such a surface is actually larger than it is for the ideal smooth sphere, because a greater fraction of the incident energy is scattered in the backward direction. Thus, even though he anticipated a 3.5 db loss from absorption, Kerr estimated that the 30 Mc/sec radar cross section of the sun would be about $\sigma = 1.5\pi R_0{}^2$, where R_0 is the radius of the photosphere. That is, he believed that the echo would be 50% stronger than if it had been returned by a smooth metal sphere the size of the optical sun. In the next section we shall have an opportunity to see whether this estimate came close to reality.

Given the value of σ for a target at a distance D, we can compute the fraction of the transmitted signal that will be returned to the antenna. If P_T is the total transmitted power, while P_D is the echo power picked up by the antenna, then

$$\frac{P_D}{P_T} = \frac{\sigma A^2}{4\pi\lambda^2 D^4}. \tag{7-1}$$

In this version of the famous *radar equation* it is assumed that a single antenna of effective area A is used for both transmission and reception.

If we accept for the moment Kerr's value of σ, we can easily compute the ratio of P_D to P_T for a solar radar experiment. Even for a large antenna of, say, 20,000 m² effective area, it turns out that $P_D/P_T = 10^{-21}$, so that if we were to transmit a million watts of power, we would get back only 10^{-15} w! Lest we overlook the immensity of this ratio, let us recall that the ratio of the length of 1 cm to the entire circumference of the earth is "only" of the order of magnitude of 10^{-10}.

THE EL CAMPO RADAR

We have seen that the Stanford experiment consisted of a relatively small number of runs "bootlegged" on an apparatus that was designed for another purpose. The first *systematic* radar observations of the sun were begun in 1961 by scientists of M.I.T.'s famous Lincoln Laboratory.[4] Their specially designed antenna covers nine acres of flat desert near El Campo, Texas, and involves more than a thousand half-wavelength dipoles suspended above a rectangular reflecting plane. Because it is much longer in the north-south direction, the array produces a fan-shaped beam whose long axis extends east and west. Needless to say, this huge antenna cannot be pointed mechanically to follow the sun, so that observations are possible only during a period of about half an hour each day as the sun crosses the local meridian. Once every few days, as the noontime altitude of the sun varies with the seasons, the elevation of the beam must be changed by manually adjusting the lengths of the 1016 cables that feed the individual dipoles, a task that takes 10 man-hours! When the beam is pointed near the zenith its angular extent is $0.7° \times 6.5°$, and the gain of the antenna is then 36 db above that of an isotropic radiator.

The El Campo transmitter generates about 500 kw of continuous-wave or "CW" power. Unlike the Stanford equipment or the usual military radars, the transmitter is not normally pulsed on and off. Instead, the radiated signal is coded by switching the transmitter back and forth between two slightly different frequencies near 38 Mc/sec. Switching occurs at pseudo-random intervals, all of which are multiples of a "basic pulse interval" that determines the range resolution of the system. As in the Stanford experiment, transmission is continued for 16 or 17 minutes; then, just as the leading edge of the echo is due to return, the antenna is quickly connected to the receiver for a similar period of listening.

Because the solar echo is still 20 to 30 db weaker than the background noise arising from the sun, the galaxy, and the equipment, it is again necessary to subject the output of the receiver to elaborate processing in order to recover the sought-after signal. In this case, 20 "range box" integrating circuits are used to store up echoes returned from 20 different distances near the anticipated range of the sun. Fed into the processing circuitry with appropriate time delays, the frequency-switching code directs each returning echo to its proper range box. The operation of the circuit is such that extraneous noise should be averaged out over a period of time to produce little or no cumulative signal.

Figure 7-2 shows the results of 32 observations made during the early months of operation of the El Campo radar. Prior to each day's run the range boxes were adjusted so that all echoes returning from the computed distance of the solar reflecting layer

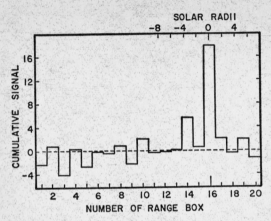

FIG. 7-2 Summary of solar observations made with the El Campo radar during the period April 19 to July 9, 1961. The signal strength is in arbitrary units. For the basic pulse interval of 8 sec used in these experiments, the range interval between successive boxes is 1.7 R_0, where R_0 is the radius of the photosphere. The scale at the top of the figure is in units of R_0. (After W. G. Abel et al.[5])

would be stored in the 16th box. In the calculations it was assumed that 38 Mc/sec waves are reflected at a height 0.5 R_0 above the photosphere, and that an additional delay of 2 sec occurs because the speed of the signal in the solar atmosphere is less than it is in free space. The figure shows that by far the largest response was obtained in the 16th range box, corresponding to just the expected solar distance.

Despite this agreement, such a measurement does not give us a highly precise determination of the distance of the sun, for it involves assumptions regarding both the depth of penetration and the speed of the radar waves in the solar atmosphere. These limitations are of course inherent in the fact that the sun is a "soft" target. The average distance from the center of the earth to the center of the sun is a vitally important quantity, known as the *astronomical unit*, which serves as a yardstick for determining all distances within the solar system. Somehow it seems incongruous that direct radar measurement of the earth-sun distance is unlikely to improve our knowledge of this crucial parameter. Fortunately, the precise laws of celestial mechanics allow us to compute the astronomical unit from any accurately known interplanetary distance, and radar has already greatly improved our knowledge of the distance of Venus, which is a hard target.

What, then, *have* we learned from solar echoes? Two significant discoveries have come out of the El Campo experiments. First, the radar cross section of the sun is highly variable, and second, the returning echoes are dispersed over an unexpectedly wide band of frequencies. During the three years from April of 1961 to April of 1964 the measured values of σ ranged all the way from zero to $16\pi R_0^2$; the "zero" values, of course, corresponded to days when no echo at all could be detected, a condition that existed 5 to 10% of the time. Even the annual averages for the three successive years showed large changes, declining from $2.2\pi R_0^2$ to $1.1\pi R_0^2$ and, finally, to $0.6\pi R_0^2$. The reader may recall that these values actually "bracket" the prediction made a decade earlier by Kerr.

Although the short-time fluctuations in σ displayed no clear correlation with sunspot numbers or other measures of solar activity, extremely large values of σ were often accompanied by distinctive increases in solar radio noise. James believes that both effects may be caused by the temporary formation of plasma tubes linking the earth with the sun across interplanetary space. According to this picture, the ion ducts serve as huge waveguides, confining the radio energy and strengthening our reception of the radar echoes as well as the natural noise of the sun itself.

The explanation of the smearing of the echoes across a wide band of frequencies is perhaps less speculative. Part of the smearing is easily understood as a consequence of the *Doppler effect* that is to be expected if the target is a rotating sphere. When a wave is reflected from a moving mirror, its frequency is altered in much the same way as if it had been emitted by a moving source, except that the frequency shift Δf for a given velocity is twice as large. In the case of the moving source, the ratio of Δf to the original frequency f is given by the well-known Doppler formula:

$$\frac{\Delta f}{f} = \pm \frac{v}{c}, \qquad (7\text{-}2)$$

where v is the component of the velocity of the source toward or away from the observer and c is the speed of light. If the source is approaching, the (+) sign applies; if it is receding, Δf is negative. For a mirror moving with a velocity v in the observer's line of sight

$$\frac{\Delta f}{f} = \pm 2 \frac{v}{c} \cdot \qquad (7\text{-}3)$$

Referring to Fig. 7-3, we see that when a radar beam strikes a rotating sphere, echoes such as A are produced by a reflecting

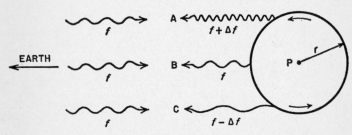

FIG. 7-3 Doppler shifts of echoes from a rotating sphere, looking down on P, the pole of rotation. The incident radar beam, of frequency f, is approaching from the left. The frequency changes in the echoes are greatly exaggerated.

surface that is moving toward the observer, while the echo at C has bounced off a receding surface. It is easy to see that at the two limbs of the target the velocity of approach or recession is $v = 2\pi r/t$, where t is the rotational period of the sphere. Thus $\Delta f = 2(f/c)(2\pi r/t)$. Obviously, all smaller values of Δf down to zero will occur between the limb and the center of the target (and between the equator and the poles), so that the echo spectrum will be a smear covering the band from $f - \Delta f$ to $f + \Delta f$. If for the sun we take $r = 1.5R_0$ and $t = 25$ days, we find that at a frequency of 38 Mc/sec, Δf is about 1 kc/sec.

How does this predicted value compare with observation? The M.I.T. scientists obtained echo spectra by making high-fidelity tape recordings of the returning signals. Later these recordings were played back through the signal-processing equipment at a number of different frequencies to produce plots such as Fig. 7-4. We see immediately that the echoes are spread over a frequency band far exceeding 1 kc/sec; the observed bandwidth, like most solar phenomena, is highly variable but it generally lies between 20 and 70 kc/sec. Clearly this is entirely inconsistent with our estimate of 1 kc/sec! What can the trouble be?

It seems obvious that solar rotation can account for only a small fraction of the measured frequency shift. The remainder of the dispersion is believed to be a Doppler effect caused by local mass motions of the coronal gases responsible for the reflections. Since Δf is found to be both positive and negative, these movements may take the form of an oscillatory upwelling and sinking of gas in response to a coronal heating cycle. However, like Fig. 7-4, nearly all of the records show a preponderance of positive values of Δf, suggesting that the oscillations are superimposed on a steady outward flow of gas. Now, such a flow is precisely what is predicted by E. N. Parker's picture of the corona

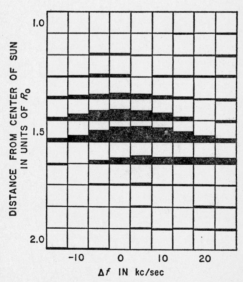

FIG. 7-4 Solar echo spectrum for October 18, 1963. The distance scale is based on an assumed delay time in the solar atmosphere, as explained in the text. Within each range interval the heights of the bars represent the relative strengths of the echoes. On this date most of the energy was returned from a small range of distances near 1.5 R_0, but on some days the spread is much greater. (After J. C. James.[4])

as undergoing a continuous, dynamic expansion that pushes gas outward through the solar system to the orbit of the earth and beyond.[6] Parker's theory even predicts a rapid acceleration of the flow near the $1.5R_0$ level, which would account for the staggering of the peaks in the figure. Thus radar has produced convincing evidence of the birth of the *solar wind*, about which we shall have a great deal to say in the next chapter.

THE FUTURE

As the sensitivity and sophistication of the technique grows, radar may well prove to be the astronomer's most powerful tool for studying gas motions within the solar corona and far out into interplanetary space. Kundu has suggested that radar waves having frequencies of hundreds of megacycles might be reflected by the shock waves speeding outward from flares, making it possible to utilize antennas of greatly increased resolution.[7] Certainly an important advance will come with the introduction of radars having beamwidths narrow enough to permit point-by-point scanning of the solar disc. Ultimately, by tracking flare-ejected plasma clouds from the explosive moment of their birth until they finally disperse in the depths of space, we may clear up some of the mysteries of the sun-earth relationships that form the topic of our final chapter.

REFERENCES

1. Smith, A. G. and Carr, T. D., *Radio Exploration of the Planetary System* (Momentum Book No. 2, D. Van Nostrand Co., Inc., Princeton, 1964).
2. Kerr, F. J., "On the Possibility of Obtaining Radar Echoes from the Sun and Planets," Proc. Inst. Radio Engrs. 40, 660-666 (1952).
3. Eshleman, V. R., Barthle, R. C., and Gallagher, P. B., "Radar Echoes from the Sun," Science 131, 329-332 (1960).
4. James, J. C., "Radar Echoes from the Sun," IEEE Trans. Military Electronics MIL-8, 210-225 (1964).
5. Abel, W. G., Chisholm, J. H., Fleck, P. L., and James, J. C., "Radar Reflections from the Sun at Very High Frequencies," J. Geophys. Res. 66, 4303-4307 (1961).
6. Parker, E. N., "The Solar Wind," Sci. Am. 210, 66-76 (April, 1964).

7. Kundu, M. R., *Solar Radio Astronomy* (John Wiley & Sons, Inc., New York, 1965).

FOR FURTHER READING

Eshleman, V. R. and Peterson, A. M., "Radar Astronomy," Sci Am. 203, 50-59 (August, 1960).

McGuire, J. B., Spangler, E. R., and Wong, L., "The Size of the Solar System," Sci. Am. 204, 64-72 (April, 1961).

8 *The Earth and the Sun*

> *"Ill blows the wind that profits nobody."*
> SHAKESPEARE, *Henry* VI

How far is it from the earth to the sun? If you were to reply that the distance is about 93 million miles, or 150 million km, you would be perfectly correct in terms of the usual astronomical definition. However, it would also be possible to argue that in a different sense your answer should be *zero*—that the two bodies are actually in contact with each other!

In recent years several lines of evidence have forced astronomers and geophysicists to abandon the old picture in which millions of miles of "empty" space separated the earth from the sun. Instead, it now appears that the orbit of the earth lies entirely within the constantly expanding solar corona, so that the atmospheres of the two bodies mingle and interact in a complex manner that has spawned a whole host of new and exciting research problems. Like so many of the most challenging enigmas of modern science, these problems transcend the tribal boundaries of the traditional disciplines and call for a concerted attack by physicists, chemists, astronomers, geophysicists, mathematicians, and even aerodynamicists.

THE RADIO SUPERCORONA

What is our evidence for such an enormously distended solar atmosphere? Even when the sun is in total eclipse, earth-bound observers cannot trace the corona much beyond 2° (or 8 times the photospheric radius R_0) from the solar limb. At that distance the corona is over a billion times fainter than the photosphere, and it simply merges into the residual glow of the eclipse-darkened sky. However, the sky is still darker at great altitudes, and by photographing an eclipse from a high-flying aircraft the British astronomer D. E. Blackwell was able to record the corona out to a distance of $28R_0$ from the center of the sun.[1]

While Blackwell's achievement is impressive, radio methods have pushed the observable fringe of the corona several times farther from the sun, thereby bringing it still closer to the earth. In 1951 the Russian radio astronomer V. V. Vitkevich called attention to the fact that every year, around the middle of June, the sun passes within $1.5°$ of the famous Crab nebula, which lies between the horns of Taurus the Bull. Since the nebula is a powerful source of radio waves, Vitkevich reasoned that its occultation by the solar atmosphere might produce observable effects that could reveal the extent of the corona. This indeed proved to be the case, and numerous occultations of "the Crab" have now been recorded at a variety of frequencies in the Soviet Union, Australia, England, France, and the United States. These observations have provided us with direct evidence of coronal material as far as $120R_0$ from the sun itself, or over half the distance to the earth.

The radio method is based on a phenomenon that is somewhat like viewing a distant source of light through a fog. As we all know from experience, the scattering that occurs in the mist greatly enlarges and dims the image of the source. Similarly, when we "view" the Crab nebula through the solar corona with a suitable interferometer its radio image is not only dimmed, but it is diffused over such a large area that it appears as an extended source with greatly reduced fringe amplitude for the reasons discussed in Chapter 3. This effect is strikingly illustrated in Fig. 8-1, where we see the change in the interferometer pattern that occurs in only two days as the nebula is covered by the denser regions of the solar atmosphere. Figure 8-2 is a summary of the results of many such observations, showing the marked day-to-day changes in the apparent intensity of the nebula as the occultation progresses.

While most observers have confined their attention to "the Crab" because of its strong radio signal, the Australian O. B. Slee has recorded coronal occultations of 13 weaker "radio stars" by using a very large and sensitive interferometer with a base-

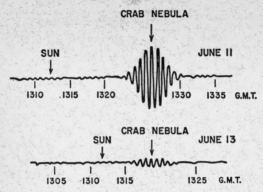

FIG. 8-1 Interferometric fringe patterns of the sun and the Crab nebula on two dates in 1956. The records were made with a lobe-switching interferometer operating at a wavelength of 1.9 m. In the lower record the sun has moved much closer to the nebula, which is then being occulted by the denser regions of the corona. The time scales refer to the local times (Greenwich Mean Time) at which various portions of the tracings were recorded. (After A. Hewish.[2])

line of no less than 10 km. These additional sources have provided scattering data for regions of the solar atmosphere that are never traversed by the Crab nebula, and three of the sources have shown evidences of scattering at distances of $100R_0$ or more from the photosphere.[3]

What is the cause of this scattering that reveals the presence of solar gases at such enormous distances? It seems probable that the radio waves are scattered by local irregularities in the electron density. Since the enlarged images of the occulted radio sources often appear to be *elongated,* it may be that the irregularities take the form of filaments stretched along lines of the sun's magnetic field. As one might expect from such a picture, the scattering shows short-time fluctuations, as well as a systematic variation with the sunspot cycle.

THE SOLAR WIND

The radio occultations have shown that the sun's gaseous envelope extends well beyond the orbit of the planet Mercury. What can we say about conditions at the orbit of the earth, which lies at an average distance of $215R_0$ from the center of

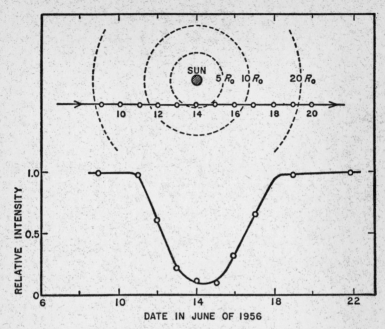

FIG. 8-2 Decrease in the apparent radio intensity of the Crab nebula as it is occulted by the solar corona. The upper half of the figure shows the position of the
nebula relative to the visible disc of the sun for the indicated dates in June, 1956.
Data recorded by the same equipment as in Fig. 8-1. (After A. Hewish.[2])

the sun? In order to answer this question the American radio
astronomer W. C. Erickson put together two bits of evidence.[4]
First he concluded that his data, together with those of other
observers, showed that the radio scattering in the corona decreases as the inverse square of the distance from the sun. Then
he noted that there are both theoretical and experimental
grounds for believing that the scattering at any point in the
solar atmosphere is simply proportional to the electron density
in that region. Combining these relationships, Erickson extrap-
olated the occultation data to the orbit of the earth and found
that the particle density there should be about 16 electrons/cm³.
It is generally presumed that the solar plasma is electrically
neutral, which would imply the presence of similar numbers of
protons.

Since Erickson's extrapolation is admittedly speculative, it is fortunate that we now have direct measurements of the particle density in space near the earth. The measurements have, of course, been made by unmanned, instrumented satellites and space probes, starting with the Soviet "Lunik 1," which was launched toward the moon in January of 1959. If we are to obtain a meaningful picture of conditions in interplanetary space, the instruments must be hurled into "deep space," many earth radii from the surface of our planet, for as we shall see in a moment, the immediate neighborhood of the earth is not at all representative of the surrounding interplanetary medium. The instruments have now shown that our region of the solar system is indeed filled with solar plasma whose density ranges from 2 to 20 protons/cm³, in good agreement with Erickson's estimate. Furthermore, the plasma is flowing outward through the solar system, just as Parker's theory of the steadily expanding corona had predicted.[5] On "quiet" days—that is, on days when the sun is relatively inactive—this *solar wind* streams past the earth's orbit at speeds ranging from 300 to 600 km/sec!

Sensitive magnetometers carried by the space vehicles show that the solar gas, as might have been expected, carries with it part of the sun's magnetic field. Curiously enough, the lines of magnetic flux are not at all parallel to the direction of flow of the solar wind itself. While the gas streams out radially from the sun, the imbedded magnetic lines are twisted so that they make an angle of about 45° with the orbit of the earth. Why should this be?

The explanation lies in the rotation of the sun, which winds the magnetic field into the huge spiral that we see in Fig. 8-3. We can understand this with the help of an ordinary rotating lawn sprinkler—in fact, the solar phenomenon is often referred to as the *water-hose effect*. Let us imagine that the disc in Fig. 8-4 is the rotating sprinkler, and that the letters *a, b, c, d, e* represent the positions of the nozzle at successively later moments in time. By the time the nozzle has rotated from *a* to *e*, a drop of water emitted at *a* has reached the point *a'*, a drop emitted at *b* has reached *b'*, and so on. Notice that the individual drops continue to move radially outward, but the *stream* is wound into

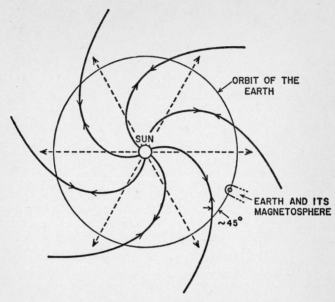

FIG. 8-3 The solar wind and the sun's distant magnetic field. The dashed lines represent the radial movement of individual particles of the solar wind, while the solid spiral arcs show the structure of the magnetic field. We are looking down from a point in space north of the plane of the earth's orbit. From such a point the sun appears to rotate in the counterclockwise direction, and the earth moves around its orbit in the same sense.

a spiral of a special kind known as an "Archimedes spiral." The form of this curve is such that its angular departure α from the radial direction is given by

$$\tan \alpha = \frac{\omega r}{v}. \tag{8-1}$$

In the case of the sun, we can imagine that the single nozzle of our illustration has been replaced by a great number of gas jets circling the rim of the rotating disc. We would then have an almost continuous sheet of gas expanding outward, but if a line of magnetic force were caught up in the stream from any one jet and dragged along by the flowing gas, it would follow the spiral path of that stream. Magnetic measurements made in 1963 and 1964 by the Imp 1 "interplanetary monitoring plat-

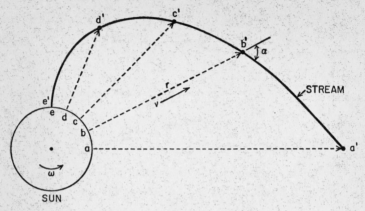

FIG. 8-4 Generation of a spiral stream by the "water-hose effect." The nozzle rotates at the angular speed ω rad/sec while squirting out fluid with a linear velocity v.

form" agree remarkably well with just such a picture.[6] In the absence of solar disturbances the intensity of the interplanetary field remained quite stable at values ranging from 4 to 7γ ($1\gamma = 10^{-5}$ gauss), and its average direction was in good agreement with the simple water-hose model. The field displayed a fibrous or filamentary structure as if it had indeed been created by the mingling of many streams, and adjacent filaments often showed a reversed magnetic sense—that is, in some cases the magnetic vector was directed inward, toward the sun, while in other cases it pointed outward (we have indicated this effect in Fig. 8-3 by drawing arrows in both directions). Apparently the solar magnetic flux in the depths of interplanetary space reflects its origin in the complex and tangled magnetic fields of the photosphere.

An unexpected confirmation of the spiral structure of the solar wind came from radio observations made for quite a different purpose. At Cambridge, A. Hewish and his colleagues noticed that certain radio stars showed peculiar, rapid variations in intensity that were unlike the usual scintillations caused by drifting irregularities in the local ionosphere.[7] The strange fluctuations proved to be associated only with radio sources of extraordinarily small angular diameter, such as the now-famous *quasi-stellar sources* or "quasars." Further investigations with the great 178 Mc/sec interferometer at Cambridge convinced the British scientists that the fluctuations were caused by the passage over the radio telescope of moving diffraction patterns that had been created by irregularities in the interplanetary medium. Just as in the optical case, the diffraction effects are smeared out and vanish unless the source is effectively a point.

Are the irregularities that are responsible for the radio diffraction merely plasma clouds streaming outward from the sun at the normal radial speed of the solar wind? Apparently not, for the cloud velocities deduced from the drift speeds of the diffraction patterns are much too small to fit this picture. However, these velocities are just what would be expected if they represent the rotation of a spiral structure at the angular speed of the sun itself! As Hewish and his associates remarked, "It seems likely that interplanetary scintillation will provide a valuable new technique, both for detecting sources of small angular extent, and for studying the interplanetary medium." It is also evident that radio astronomers can no longer neglect the possible effects of this medium on their observations.

THE MAGNETOSPHERE

What happens when the solar wind collides with the earth? We now know that the pressure of the earth's magnetic field drives back the solar wind and carves out a broad cavity in the interplanetary medium, within which the earth floats in relative serenity. The interior of the cavity is appropriately known as the *magnetosphere*, for it is dominated by the terrestrial magnetic field, and its outer boundary is called the *magnetopause*. In Fig. 8-5 we see these features as they are depicted by theory and by experimental evidence from satellites and space probes.

On the sunward side of the earth the location of the magnetopause reflects a delicate balance between the pressure of the impinging solar wind and the resisting pressure of the terrestrial magnetic field. The streaming solar plasma exerts a pressure p_0 that is given (approximately) by

$$p_0 = \tfrac{1}{2}nMv^2, \tag{8-2}$$

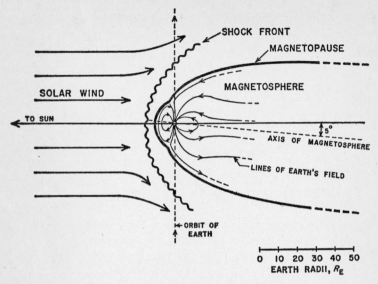

FIG. 8-5 The terrestrial magnetosphere and its environment. Because of the earth's orbital motion, the tail of the magnetosphere does not point straight away from the sun but is deflected about 5°. The famous Van Allen radiation belts occupy part of the magnetospheric cavity, but to avoid confusion they are not shown here.

where n is the number of particles per unit volume, M is the mass of each particle, and v is the velocity of the solar wind.* Let us take typical values, such as $n = 5/\text{cm}^3$ and $v = 500$ km/sec or 5×10^7 cm/sec. Since the solar plasma is composed largely of protons, together with accompanying electrons of negligible mass, we can let M equal the mass of the proton, 1.67×10^{-24} gm. Under these conditions we find that $p_0 \cong 10^{-8}$ dyne/cm^2.

Driven back by the impact of the solar wind, the earth's magnetic field reacts by exerting a magnetic pressure

$$p_{\text{m}} = B^2/8\pi. \qquad (8\text{-}3)$$

Here B is the strength in gauss of the compressed field in the region of impact. Equilibrium is of course established when $p_{\text{m}} = p_0$; that is, when the terrestrial magnetic field on the sun-

---

* The numerical factor in Eq. (8–2) ranges from $\frac{1}{2}$ to 2, depending upon the assumptions made regarding the way in which the solar wind is reflected or deflected by the magnetosphere.

ward side of the earth has been compressed until $B^2/8\pi \cong 10^{-8}$ dyne/cm^2. We see that this occurs when $B = 5 \times 10^{-4}$ gauss or 50γ, a value that is in good agreement with the measurements made by Imp 1 just inside the magnetopause.

Because the solar wind rushes past the earth at supersonic speed, the magnetosphere is preceded by the shock wave that is shown in Fig. 8-5. Although this wave is quite analogous to the shock wave that is generated by a supersonic aircraft, it is not really a "sound wave." If a wave is to exist in a gas—or for that matter in any mechanical medium—the molecules must somehow *communicate* with each other in order to establish and maintain the necessary cooperative motions. In an ordinary gas this communication occurs through frequent collisions, but the interplanetary medium is so tenuous that collisions are extremely rare. Instead, the ions are linked to each other by the accompanying magnetic field, and the resulting waves are therefore not acoustic, but of a type known as *hydromagnetic*. We can best visualize such waves by picturing the lines of magnetic force as stretched elastic cords. When the field is disturbed, the cords are set into transverse oscillation, like the famous "vibrating string" of the physics texts, and the surrounding plasma is forced to share the motion.

Our understanding of the magnetosphere on the night-time side of the earth is much more limited. Somewhat surprisingly, space probes show that the magnetospheric cavity streams far out into space to form a long, diverging tail, estimates of whose length have ranged all the way from a few dozen earth radii to as much as 50 astronomical units![8] Space scientists were even more astonished when the Imp 1 magnetometers indicated that the moon is followed by a similar magnetospheric wake in apparent defiance of the long-held belief that our natural satellite has no magnetic field.[6] The lunar tail seems to extend to at least 150 moon radii, which is insufficient to reach the earth.

Although the magnetosphere stands as a buffer between the earth and the solar wind, it cannot shield us completely from the space environment. We saw in Chapter 5 that solar disturbances are accompanied by outpourings of radio energy. At the same time the sun bombards the earth with intense bursts of X-rays, which are, of course, unaffected by the terrestrial magnetic field. Striking our atmosphere, these energetic photons create a new layer of ions below the normal ionosphere. Because this layer is a powerful absorber of radio waves, it may suddenly disrupt vital short-wave communications over much of the sunlit hemisphere for an hour or more.

It also seems that solar eruptions inject great "gusts" into the steadily flowing solar wind. Racing outward at speeds of 1500 km/sec, these plasma clouds reach the earth in about 30 hours and subject the protecting magnetosphere to a severe buffeting, which results in further compression of the geomagnetic field as well as the possible generation of hydromagnetic waves. As the plasma clouds swirl by the magnetosphere, they induce great systems of electrical currents with their associated magnetic fields.

Inevitably, symptoms of this lofty turmoil are felt at ground level. Often the terrestrial magnetic field fluctuates erratically in both intensity and direction, and we say that a *magnetic storm* is in progress. Charged particles, perhaps from the Van Allen radiation belts, are "dumped" into the atmosphere to create the astonishing displays of light that are known as *aurorae*. Unfortunately, these beautiful exhibitions are often accompanied by severe disturbances of high-latitude radio communications, and by marked scintillation of celestial radio sources.

Even more serious from the point of view of the radio engineer is the *ionospheric storm,* which is a frequent companion of the other phenomena. In such a storm the vital F_2 layer of the ionosphere is weakened or destroyed, and the myriad communication links that depend upon the reflection of signals from this layer are rendered useless for long periods of time. One of the simplest proofs of the control that the sun exercises over our communications is the fact that radio propagation conditions tend to repeat themselves after 27 days—that is, after the sun has turned once on its axis.

SOLAR COSMIC RAYS

Of all the hazards of a manned space voyage, chance irradiation by high-energy particles from the sun looms as the danger

most difficult to control.[9] In a single year at the peak of the
solar cycle the sun may spew forth as many as 15 streams of
particles, largely protons, whose individual energies range from
millions to billions of electron volts (an ordinary solar wind
proton has an energy of only 1000 ev). For historical reasons we
call these energetic particles *solar cosmic rays,* although it is now
clear that they differ in many ways from the "real" cosmic rays
that enter the solar system from the depths of interstellar space.[10]

Since most of the solar cosmic rays are able to penetrate the
magnetosphere, we owe a great debt to our atmosphere for
stopping the rest of these biologically dangerous particles. In
deep space this protection is completely absent, and the stringent
weight restrictions in space vehicles make it impractical to
substitute artificial shielding of the necessary thickness. It has
been estimated that during the last sunspot cycle there were
six or eight solar cosmic-ray events of sufficient intensity to dis-
able the crew of a space vehicle unlucky enough to be caught in
them. Prolonged missions in deep space may have to be under-
taken in the years around sunspot minimum, when the prob-
ability of a damaging cosmic-ray outburst is slight.

There is no doubt that solar cosmic rays are born in large
flares, although 80% of the flares of importance 2+ or greater
give rise to no detectable particles. Apparently the flare must be
of a rather special kind, one characteristic of which seems to be
the presence of strong Type IV radio emission. In Chapter 5
we saw that the synchrotron process plays an important role in
such emission, indicating that the parent flare has somehow
accelerated electrons to relativistic velocities. Perhaps the same
mechanism that energizes the electrons also accelerates the
cosmic-ray particles to their enormous energies.

Typically, the cosmic-ray intensity at the earth reaches its
peak one or two hours after the brightest phase of the optical
flare. The bombardment generally continues with gradually
diminishing intensity for hours or even for days, showing much
the same sort of lifetime as the Type IV emission itself. It has
been suggested that many of the cosmic rays are initially trapped
in the magnetic bottle that represents the site of at least part of

the radio emission (Fig. 5-13), and that they slowly leak out of this bottle to prolong the event.

Curiously enough, outbursts of solar cosmic rays can be detected merely by monitoring the steady radio noise from our own galaxy. Generated by synchrotron emission from electrons spiraling in the galactic magnetic field, this signal arrives from all parts of the sky with sufficient strength to be recorded by a very simple radio telescope known as a *riometer*. When energetic protons enter our atmosphere, they have much the same effect as the solar X-rays in creating a temporary absorbing layer beneath the normal ionosphere. This layer strongly attenuates the incoming galactic radio signal and, as we see in Fig. 8-6, causes

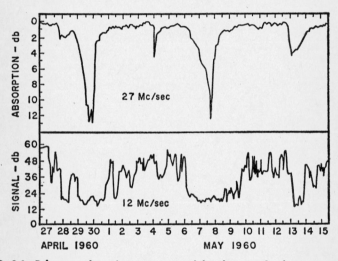

FIG. 8-6 Polar cap absorption events caused by showers of solar protons. The upper curve is a riometer record from Thule, Greenland, showing four sharp decreases in the 27 Mc/sec "cosmic radio noise" received from our Milky Way galaxy. Below is a simultaneous record of man-made shortwave radio signal strength over a path linking Thule and College, Alaska. Note that each major polar cap absorption is accompanied by severe fading of the artificial signal, indicating that communications might be interrupted for periods of several days. (After R. D. Egan.[11])

a sudden drop in its recorded level. This effect is especially severe in the polar regions, where the terrestrial magnetic field guides charged particles into the atmosphere instead of repelling them. Here the phenomenon is called a *polar cap blackout,* for it may completely disrupt radio communications for several days.

Because of their implications for the huge space program, as well as their effect on communications, solar cosmic rays have assumed considerable practical importance. Needless to say, vigorous efforts are being made to develop methods of forecasting their occurrence. At present these methods are in their infancy, but this should scarcely surprise us when we stop to consider the notorious uncertainties that still attend the age-old problem of forecasting tomorrow's weather! Nevertheless, greatly increased understanding will finally emerge from the current radio and optical assault on the complex problems of solar physics, and man will have taken one more important step in his endless struggle to master his environment.

REFERENCES

1. Blackwell, D. E., "The Zodiacal Light," Sci. Am. 203, 54-63 (July, 1960).
2. Hewish, A., "The Scattering of Radio Waves in the Solar Corona," Monthly Not. Roy. Astron. Soc. London 118, 534-546 (1958).
3. Slee, O. B., "Observations of the Solar Corona out to 100 Solar Radii," Monthly Not. Roy. Astron. Soc. London 123, 223-231 (1961).
4. Erickson, W. C., "The Radio-Wave Scattering Properties of the Solar Corona," Astrophys. J. 139, 1290-1311 (1964).
5. Parker, E. N., "The Solar Wind," Sci. Am. 210, 66-76 (April, 1964).
6. Ness, N. F., Scearce, C. S., and Seek, J. B., "Initial Results of the Imp 1 Magnetic Field Experiment," J. Geophys. Res. 69, 3531-3569 (1964).
7. Hewish, A., Scott, P. F., and Wills, D., "Interplanetary Scintillation of Small Diameter Radio Sources," Nature 203, 1214-1217 (1964).
8. Dessler, A. J., "Length of Magnetospheric Tail," J. Geophys. Res. 69, 3913-3918 (1964).
9. Freier, Phyllis and Webber, W. R., "Radiation Hazard in Space from Solar Particles," Science 142, 1587-1592 (1963).
10. Anderson, K. A., "Solar Particles and Cosmic Rays," Sci. Am. 202, 64-71 (June, 1960).
11. Egan, R. D., "Thule to College 12 Mc Propagation During the April and May 1960 Intense Polar Cap Absorption Events," in *The Effect of Disturbances of Solar Origin on Communications,* edited by G. J. Gassmann (Pergamon Press, Inc., New York, 1963), pp. 47-58.

FOR FURTHER READING

Chapman, S., *Solar Plasma, Geomagnetism and Aurora* (Gordon and Breach, New York, 1964).

Gassmann, G. J., editor, *The Effect of Disturbances of Solar Origin on Communications* (Pergamon Press, Inc., New York, 1963).

Hess, W. N., editor, *The Physics of Solar Flares* (U.S. Government Printing Office, Washington, 1964), pp. 215-297.

Hewish, A., "Radio Investigation of the Solar Corona and the Interplanetary Medium," in *Solar System Radio Astronomy*, edited by J. Aarons (Plenum Press, Inc., New York, 1965), pp. 255-266.

LeGalley, D. P. and Rosen, A., editors, *Space Physics* (John Wiley & Sons, Inc., New York, 1964).

Parker, E. N., *Interplanetary Dynamical Processes* (John Wiley & Sons, Inc., New York, 1963).

Tilson, S., "The Solar Atmosphere," Intern. Sci. Tech., 20-31 (January, 1963).

SOME USEFUL CONSTANTS AND RELATIONSHIPS

Ångstrom unit: $1\text{Å} = 10^{-8}$ cm

Astronomical unit (mean distance of sun): $d = 1.496 \times 10^8$ km

Boltzmann constant: $k = 1.380 \times 10^{-16}$ erg/deg

1 Cal/sec = 4.185 w

Earth's equatorial radius = 6.378×10^3 km

Electron

  Charge: $e = 1.602 \times 10^{-19}$ coulomb = 4.803×10^{-10} esu

  Mass: $m = 0.9108 \times 10^{-27}$ gm

1 Electron volt = 1.602×10^{-12} erg

Gamma: $1\ \gamma = 10^{-5}$ gauss

Light, Speed of: $c = 2.998 \times 10^{10}$ cm/sec

1 Light year = 9.460×10^{12} km

1 Mile = 1.609 km

Moon

  Mean angular diameter = 31.6' of arc

  Mean distance = 3.844×10^5 km

  Radius = 1.738×10^3 km

Proton, mass: $M = 1.673 \times 10^{-24}$ gm

1 Radian = $57.30° = 2.063 \times 10^5$ sec of arc

Sun

  Mean angular diameter = 32.0' of arc

  Mass = 1.989×10^{33} gm

  Radius of photosphere: $R_0 = 6.960 \times 10^5$ km

Solar constant: $H = 2.00$ cal/cm^2/min

1 Year = 3.156×10^7 sec

APPENDIX 2

SYMBOLS AND ABBREVIATIONS USED FREQUENTLY IN THIS BOOK

A = Angstrom
B = magnetic field in gauss
c = cycle
c = speed of light
cal = calorie
cm = centimeter
cps = cycles per second
db = decibel
e = charge on electron
ev = electron volt
f = frequency
ft = foot
f_0 = critical frequency
gm = gram
in. = inches
K = Kelvin (temperature)

kc = kilocycle
km = kilometer
kw = kilowatt
λ = wavelength
m = meter
Mc = megacycle
Mev = millions of electron volts
min = minute
mm = millimeter
Ω = solid angle
rad = radian
S = flux density (w/m^2/cps)
sec = second
sterad = steradian
T = absolute temperature (°K)
w = watt

Index